Missionary Stories
to Play and Tell

Missionary Stories
to Play and Tell

edited by NINA MILLEN

FRIENDSHIP PRESS
new york

TYPE: *Text, Linotype Granjon, 11 pt., leaded 1 pt.*
Display, Bernhard Tango

COMPOSITION, PRINTING, AND BINDING: *Sowers Printing*
Company, Lebanon, Pa.

JACKETS AND PAPER COVERS: *Affiliated Lithographers, Inc.,*
New York

PAPER: *S. D. Warren's #66 Antique*

DESIGNERS: *Format, Margery W. Smith*
Binding, Louise E. Jefferson

Library of Congress Catalog Card Number: 58-12772

Contents

1083449

AFRICA

ASIA

vi *Contents*

China

Light Pictures (J)

The Three Surprises (P)

India

The Lights of Christmas (P)

The Church That Was Builded by Moonlight (J)

Iran

The Mischief Maker (P)

Japan

Two Bright Eyes (P)

Sadao and the Story Man (P)

Korea

Bricks and a Dream (J)

Philippines

Pablo Helps with the Writing (P)

The Independent Hen (J)

NEW ZEALAND

THE AMERICAS

"I See It Coming"

IN HOSI'S village in Africa, there were stories every night— stories for the whole village, and just as certain to come as night itself.

When the meal of corn mush and greens was finished and the mush baskets washed and put away, Hosi, who was nine, sat outside the door of his little round home to watch and wait. Beside every house in the village circle, he could see the smoke of the cooking fires lazily drifting over the grass roofs. While he sat there, the sun dropped behind the trees. Hosi's village in Angola was so near the equator that the sun went to bed regularly at six o'clock. Then darkness came quickly.

Now all around the village, boys and girls and mothers and fathers waited outside their houses for their chief to lead them to the *onjango*. The *onjango* was the place where the stories were told. It was a big circle with a round grass roof over it held up by posts. All around it, except for the entrance, was a low wall of sticks and clay. A fire burned brightly in the center. "The story fire," Hosi called it.

The chief, wearing his red blanket with the bells on it, came forth from his house. He and his headmen led the procession to the *onjango*. The chief and his headmen sat on stools near the fire. Then all the village people sat down, filling the whole space inside the wall.

Stories didn't come first. Oh, no! First of all, there were the important matters of the tribe to bring before the chief. Sapunga had lost one of his best cows. Sapunga's brother spoke up loudly to say that a big leopard that was prowling around the village must have killed it. Then there was talking backward and forward, and in that talking it was proved that the brother himself had stolen Sapunga's cow. The brother hung his head in shame when the chief said that the cow must be returned.

Lisi's baby was sick. It was burning with fever and getting worse. Surely that was a sign the spirits were angry.

"Has anyone forgotten to set out food for the spirits of the tribe?" asked the chief in a very solemn voice.

Hosi looked all around the circle. There was fear on every face. At the very mention of spirits everyone was afraid, for the people believed that those who had once lived in the village and were now dead were the spirits of the tribe. Of course, those spirits must be fed and kept happy, or else they would be angry and send dreadful trouble, like sickness or bad crops.

Hosi was glad that he had seen his mother set out a basket of good corn mush for the spirits that very night. After she had dipped up a little woven basket of mush for each member of her family, she had filled another basket, too. She had taken it outside the house, where she had set it down and had called and beckoned the spirits to come and eat.

The chief was assured that no one had forgotten to feed the spirits. "Then let the witch doctor be summoned tomorrow," he said. "Let him speak with the spirits and find out why they have sent sickness."

The bells on the chief's blanket tinkled louder and louder as he gave each of his decisions as head of the tribe. At last there was a mighty shake of his blanket and a mighty tinkling of the bells. His judgments had been completed. There was a bustle of excitement in the *onjango*. Sapunga built up the fire. It was time for stories!

A quietness settled over the *onjango*—the exciting kind of quiet that you can hardly stand, because you know that something is coming out of it. You didn't know who was going to tell the story—you just waited—waited—waited—until—

"I see it coming!" said Sekulu. Those were the exciting words with which a story always began. "I see it coming!"

"Let it come!" shouted all the others.

So Sekulu went on. "Once there was a terrible drought in all the land."

Hosi wriggled with pleasure. It was the turtle story! His favorite story! He had heard it again and again. Among all the stories of the *onjango*—all the stories of the tribe, all the fables of the animals—he felt that it was the very best. He began to clap his hands softly to show his pleasure, as he leaned forward to hear it once more.

In the next few years Hosi heard that turtle story many times in the *onjango*. Then a great change came.

When Hosi was fourteen, he had a chance to go to school in a village seven miles away. It was a strange experience for Hosi to sit and eat at a table with boys from other villages. It was strange to unroll his sleeping mat at night in a room with many others. It was strangest of all to open a book and try to read.

At first Hosi didn't like school. He was homesick for the little round hut that was home and the cooking fire beside which he squatted to eat his basket of mush. Reading was hard. More than once he decided to run away. More than once he planned how he would slip off into the jungle and follow the trail back to his home village. There was just one thing that kept him at the school—stories.

Every evening in the big room there were stories—new ones that Hosi had never heard in all his evenings in the *onjango*

—stories about other tribes that didn't live in Africa but in faraway lands. There was the story of Joseph and the story of David and the story of Samuel.

"That would sound good in the *onjango*," Hosi would say to himself about each new story. He would try to remember it so that he could tell it in the *onjango* at home. Sometimes after he had gone to bed at night, he would practice telling a story.

"I see it coming!" he would whisper to himself.

Soon Hosi learned that all these stories had been written down. They were in a book called the Bible. They could be read in his own language. If only he could learn to read!

Suddenly Hosi began to surprise his teacher by reading very well! He was thinking of the day when he would take the stories to the *onjango*. He even dreamed about it.

One night Hosi dreamed that he had returned to his village. With the Bible in his hand, he went before the chief in his dream and said, "O Chief, I have brought a book of many stories for the *onjango*."

In his dream the chief smiled and said, "I myself will listen to the new stories." And Hosi started to read a story to the chief when someone pulled him back. It was Wangu tugging at his sleeping blanket and saying, "Get up, get up, or you will be late for morning mush." Hosi came out of his dream and jumped up quickly, for if he were late, he would have to hoe an extra hour in the corn, and these days he wanted all his time for reading.

There was a white teacher at the school. When he saw how Hosi wanted to take the Bible stories to his village, he arranged for him to go to another school where he could study the Bible more thoroughly. "Then you will be better able to tell your village about it," said the white teacher.

So it came about that years passed before Hosi returned to his village. When he did, it was ruled by a new chief who did not know him. The chief was angry that Hosi had come. He feared him because he could read a book.

"Do not fear me," said Hosi. "The Book I bring speaks of Suku, our God. It tells of his love for us."

"I do not want your Book. I shall drive you out of the village," threatened the chief.

Hosi was very sad. Now that he had returned, he longed more than ever to tell his people about Suku's love for them. His people had always believed that Suku the Creator had made heaven and earth and all things. But they did not know of Suku's love and care for them. If they knew, they would no longer fear the evil spirits.

One evening Hosi went to the *onjango*. Sad and discouraged, he sat among his people. He saw that the chief looked displeased.

"He fears what I may say," thought Hosi.

Someone built up the fire. All sat waiting for a story. As Hosi looked into the fire, suddenly he thought of what to do. His favorite turtle story would help him.

"I see it coming!" said Hosi.

"Let it come!" said the others in chorus.

So Hosi began. "Once there was a terrible drought in all the land. First the little streams dried up, and the springs dried up, and even the rivers dried up. The tall grass crackled in the hot wind. Even the jungle was parched and brown. All the animals were very thirsty and many died.

"Then it was that the elephant, great and important chief of the jungle that he was, called a council of all the animals. From all parts of the jungle they came dragging along, red-eyed and weary and thirsty and cross, to decide what might be done about the terrible drought, and to consult as to where they might find some water. The tiger came, and the leopard and the deer and the giraffe and the hippopotamus, looking more wrinkled and dusty than ever. And the elephant shook his powerful head from side to side, and asked if there was anything that could be done. But all the animals hung their heads in discouragement, for each had been searching far and wide, and none had found water.

"At last the turtle appeared at the council, and crawling into the circle, he said, 'O elephant, great chief of the jungle, listen to me, and I will tell you where there is a spring.'

"But the elephant looked with scorn on the turtle. 'Hush, foolish one,' he said, and lifting him on the end of his trunk, he hurled him over his head and far back into the jungle.

"The turtle righted himself, and crawled back to the council circle. Again he stood before the chief, and said, 'Great and honorable one, in my travels I have seen the spring. Come with me—' But before he could finish speaking, the elephant again tossed him on his trunk and again threw him far back into the jungle.

"The turtle almost gave up. But when he thought of the fresh water that would give life to all, he decided to try once more, and the third time he appeared, the tiger said, 'O chief, it can do no harm to listen to the turtle. Let us follow him, and if there is a spring, our lives will be saved.'

"Thus it was decided, and all the animals set out in a weary, solemn procession, following the turtle far, far back into the jungle. At last they came to a hole from which bubbled a fresh spring of water. Then every animal drank, for the spring was never dry. After each one had drunk, he turned to the turtle to say, '*Twa-pa-ndu-la,* thank you.' And the turtle was happy because he had saved their lives."

Everyone in the *onjango* was glad to hear Hosi tell the old and favorite story. They smiled and clapped their hands softly.

The chief was pleased, too, and a little proud that Hosi belonged to this village and could tell such a good story.

Then Hosi took the Bible in his two hands and held it while he addressed the chief, saying, "O Chief, I have brought a message for my people. Like the spring, it will bring new life to our village. And if you drive me away, I will come back. Like the turtle, I will come back again and again and again."

When the chief saw how earnest Hosi was, he decided that the village must listen, and he said. "We will listen to your message. In the *onjango* we will listen."

Every evening after that, in the *onjango*, Hosi told stories from the Book. All the people listened to him. As they heard the stories over and over, they came to believe that Suku was a God of love. They no longer feared the evil spirits, and all the village came to live in a better, happier way.

—*Gertrude Jenness Rinden. From "Around the World with the Bible."*

NEW WORDS IN THE STORY

Hosi	HOH-see
Lisi	LEE-zee
onjango	ohn-JAHN-goh
Sapunga	sah-POON-gah
Sekulu	seh-KOO-loo
Suku	soo-KOO
Twa-pa-ndu-la	twah-pahn-DOO-lah
Wangu	wahn-GOO

℘eanuts for Church

TO MONEZIP, in her village in the great African forest, Sunday was the best day of all the week. At least it was in the dry season. In the rainy season it was different, and Monezip wished it didn't have to be different.

In the dry season, on Sundays, when the first streaks of light appeared in the sky and life stirred in the great forest, the steady beat of a drum rolled through the trees.

> Bote . . . bese . . . be . . . zu,
> Everybody come,
> Come to worship God!

The drum call wakened Monezip. It wakened Mother and Father and small Ze and all the village people.

In the dry season, each Sunday when the drum sounded through the forest, Monezip was the first in her family to get up and make ready for church.

It was a long walk through the forest. The path led through thick bushes, down steep banks, and across small streams. Many times on the walk Monezip wished for a church of her own in her own village.

On the way through the forest everyone sang. Father led the songs and sang what was in his heart. The others repeated his words like a chorus.

God's green plant grows in the garden!
Yes, it's God's green plant that grows in the garden.

The plant is hoed with a little short hoe.
Yes, the little hoe helps God's plants to grow.

The plant is warmed by God's great sun.
Yes, the sunshine helps God's plant to grow.

Monezip said to Mother, "Singing makes the way seem shorter."

In the rainy season, also, the sound of the drum rolled through the forest on Sundays. But Monezip could not go to church. Then the small streams became rushing rivers. Water covered forest paths. Bridges were washed away. Monezip wanted to go to church, but Father was firm.

"No," he said. "The path through the forest is not safe for small feet."

In the rainy season Monezip wished more than ever that she had a church of her own, but she kept her wish to herself. That is, she kept it to herself until one day when Pastor Ela came to visit at her house.

Then she spoke out to Pastor Ela. "In the rainy season I can't go to church. I wish I had my own church in the village. Then I could hear stories of Jesus every Sunday."

Pastor Ela answered, "If people love the stories of Jesus enough, they will build their own church."

After Pastor Ela left, Monezip said to Father, "We could try to build a church."

Father talked to the men about building a church, but each one gave an excuse.

"We have no plot of cleared ground."

"Who would do the work?"

"How could we pay for a teacher like Pastor Ela?"

Not one thought the village could possibly have a church of its own.

Monezip kept remembering Pastor Ela's words. She said them again and again to herself. "If people love the stories of Jesus enough, they will build their own church."

One day Monezip said to Mother and Father, "I could raise peanuts and sell them. With the money I could buy a Bible for the church."

The whole family caught the idea.

Mother said, "I could weave a cloth for the pulpit."

Small Ze added, "I could help, too."

Father said, "I could help clear the ground. I will find out if others will help also."

Father went to the village headman and said, "If each person will do something to help, I am sure the church can be built."

That evening the whole matter was talked over by the men of the village.

The headman said, "I will sell two of my sheep. The money will buy nails and wood for the door."

A young man just home from the mission school said, "I have learned the carpenter's trade. I'll carve the pulpit."

Mombo, the drummer, said, "Our church must have its own drum. I will make it."

Every Christian in the village thought of some way to help.

When the dry season came, the work on the church began. Father was put in charge.

When the stars formed a certain pattern in the sky above, Mother said the sign was right for planting. "You may come to the gardens with me now," she told Monezip.

"I'll do the work myself," Monezip said. She raked her plot and planted her peanut seed. As the weeks passed and the plants grew high, she hoed and weeded and watched over them. At last the peanuts were ripe. She pulled the tangled roots from the ground and spread the peanuts out in the sun to dry.

When the shells were dry, Ze helped to break them open.

Monezip picked out the plump firm nuts. She heaped the shelled nuts in her basket, getting them ready to be taken to the market.

Over the basket she spread a white cloth.

Monezip and Mother walked to the market, an hour's walk away. At the market Monezip spread out the peanuts on the cloth on the ground. The people who passed bought them, a measure at a time.

At last all the nuts were sold. Monezip showed Mother the coins she had earned.

Mother said, "Tie them in your head cloth. Then they will be safe."

Monezip did as Mother said, and on the way home she reached up many times and touched the blue cloth to make sure that the coins were still there.

At home Father counted the coins and told Monezip, "It is a big gift for you to earn all by yourself." He unlocked the wooden chest, and Monezip placed the coins inside to keep them safe.

Meanwhile men cut trees, cleared the ground, and measured off the plot for the church.

Ze and the small children brought water in their cans and poured it on heaps of loose earth. The older children puddled it with bare feet and made thick mud.

Men mixed sand with the mud and threw the mixture against strips of wood tied between posts stuck deep into the ground. There it dried and formed the hard mud walls. With white clay they painted the walls inside and out.

Other men built a high platform beside the church and used heavy vine ropes to pull the new drum into place.

When all the work was finished, the workers went to their homes to sleep and to rest.

The next morning, when the earliest streaks of light appeared over the forest trees, Old Mombo climbed the high platform and began to tap his drum. He beat out the message for all to hear.

> It's Sunday. Get awake!
> The words of God are here.
>
> Come and get them! Come and get them!
> No one else can get them for you.
>
> You must come!
> It's Sunday! It's Sunday!

Monezip heard the drum call. Mother, Father, and small Ze heard it. All the village people heard it and came, bringing their gifts into the new church, which had been decorated with palm leaves and flowers.

The people walked down the aisle in a procession. Some carried their gifts on their heads, some in their hands. They waited in front while two strong men brought the pulpit and set it in its place.

Mother stepped forward and arranged her cloth across it. The people placed their gifts upon it.

Monezip put her coins on the cloth, too. She felt that it was a Bible she was placing there.

Now Sunday would be the best day of the week for her in both the dry season and the rainy season. Now she could hear stories every Sunday in her own church.

> —*Elizabeth Allstrom. From "The Round Window."*

NEW WORDS IN THE STORY

Bote bese be zu	boht-ah bah-seh bah zoo
Ela	ay-lah
Mombo	mahm-boh
Monezip	mahn-ah-zip
Ze	zeh

By the Side of the Trail

YOMBA found that walking six steps and running two kept him ahead of the bigger boys as they went along the trail through the rain forest of tropical West Africa. On their walk from Union College of Bunumbu to the little churchless village where they held a service once a week, the boys liked to sing the native songs of Africa, usually with new Christian words because the old words were of things they had left behind when they became Christians. Sometimes they sang spirituals that the missionaries had taught them. Singing made the trip more pleasant.

Yomba had his reasons for wanting to lead as they walked the trail. First, he liked to prove that he was big enough to go to the village with the high school boys—Sahr, Mani, Tomba, Dudu, and Sute. Yomba's big brother Sahr had let him come along just this once. Second, the leader could see more. If an elephant or a bush pig lurked about, the first boy would be the one to see it before it disappeared into the jungle. Even monkeys were more fun when you came on them suddenly. So far, the only discovery Yomba had made was a rope of driver ants stretching across the trail. Because he could smell the ants, Yomba found them in time to leap across them and warn the other boys. No African boy in his right mind would disturb sharp-stinging driver ants.

"The village is near," Yomba called back as the trail entered cultivated fields. "I see boys setting rope traps."

"They're after coney rabbits and other small animals that suck sap from rice stalks," Sahr answered.

Soon the trail led into the clearing around the village. Men and women were working with their short-handled hoes. Boys and girls with slingshots were driving away the ricebirds that liked to feed on the crops.

"I wish I lived here," Yomba called over his shoulder, as he watched the village children standing on platforms raised high enough to give them a long view of the fields. Yomba wanted to try a slingshot, but he knew the big boys would expect him to keep going.

The village was in sight now. Yomba could see the conical thatched roofs of its wattle-and-daub houses in their grove of tall cottonwood trees.

"What's that beside the trail?" Yomba pointed at something ahead of them near the edge of the village.

"Just a pile of rags," said Mani, "soaked from being left out in the rains." This was the rainy season when anything not under cover grew soggy in short order.

Yomba noticed something queer about the rags. They stirred a little, even though there was no breeze. "The rags are moving," he said. "There's something alive inside them."

Dudu stepped ahead to look. "It's a woman by the side of the trail," he said.

"She looks sick," said Sute.

In a few steps they were beside the tiny old woman. She hid her face and tried to cover herself with her rags.

"Why don't you go home to the village?" Sahr asked.

The woman raised her two arms. She had no hands—only scarred and ugly stumps. The boys saw that she had that most dread of all diseases, leprosy. They knew why she was an outcast from her village, sitting alone by the side of the trail.

They wanted to say something cheerful, but what was there to say? They stood a minute, embarrassed and uncomfortable, then walked on to the village.

Dudu and Sute went to the open space at the center of the village. They stood near the thatched court building, waiting for people to gather. The other boys wandered among the small round huts whose thatched roofs hung low to protect the mud-daubed walls from the rain. The boys stopped at the narrow doorways to greet the people and let them know it was time for worship. They spoke to women working in their yards and to children playing in the space between the huts. They sent children running out to the workers in the fields to say that the boys from the school had come.

Gradually the villagers gathered under the thatched roof of the court building and in the open space about it. All the Christians came, and some who were wondering about becoming Christians. A few others joined them just to see what was happening, though they did not intend to give up the familiar religion of their ancestors. Even one of the Muslims, who lived at the edge of the village, came but did not expect to learn anything from the Christian boys.

As the boys preached and prayed and sang with the people, they could not forget the sick woman by the side of the trail. They found themselves looking in her direction. They watched her hitch closer to the trail, the better to hear what was going on in the village where she was no longer welcome.

After the service, the boys asked, "Who is the little woman with leprosy by the side of the trail?"

"She is mother of a wife of the chief," was the answer. The boys knew the chief. He was not a Christian. Neither were his wives.

"Why doesn't her daughter help her?" the boys asked.

"She does not want to catch leprosy and bring it back to her children," said one of the villagers.

"And she is busy working in her house and in the chief's fields," said another. "He has much work for his wives."

The boys knew they could not tell the villagers what a wife of the chief should do. They wished there were another trail from the village. They dreaded walking past the woman again. It was hard to feel so much like helping and not to know what to do.

The woman hitched away from the trail before the boys reached her. They greeted her and hesitated. They could think of nothing worth saying, so went on toward home.

Somehow they did not feel like singing or talking. Silently they walked past the village fields and through the rain forest. Silently they came into the clearing around their town and entered their dormitory. The teachers asked if they were all right. It was so strange for them to come home quietly. Usually their songs could be heard long before the sound of their footsteps.

"We are all right," Dudu assured their teachers. Their trouble was nothing they could talk about. There were many people in West Africa who had leprosy, but it was different when you saw one who had been cast out of her village.

The boys went to bed in their dormitory. Sleep did not come to any of them. When they closed their eyes, they saw the sick old woman alone by the side of the trail in the rainy season—no shelter, no food, little clothing and that not dry. When the other boys were all asleep, the six who had walked the trail that day were wide-awake and tossing. Before long, the six boys gathered around Sahr's bed to talk.

"We must make some plan to help that woman," said Dudu.

"There's no sleep for us till we do," agreed Sute.

"Somebody should take her to a hospital," said Mani.

"But where?" asked Sahr sensibly. "It's many miles to the nearest hospital, and I've heard they have no way even there to care for people who have leprosy."

"How would we get her to a hospital?" asked Dudu. "Even if we had a car, we could not drive the jungle trail to the village. She could not walk on her stumps of legs."

"Besides," said Tomba, who knew how villagers felt, "an old woman would be homesick away from the fields and forests she has always known."

"Right," agreed Mani. "We must help her where she is."

At last the boys made their plan. They tiptoed through the dormitory to knock at the door of the principal's bedroom. Fortunately, he was the sort of man who was ready to talk with his students at any time of day or night. He rubbed his eyes, sat up in bed, and called a wondering "Come in!"

Sahr told the story of the woman, the others putting in bits he forgot. He ended, "We have three requests."

"Yes?" encouraged the principal.

"We want a holiday tomorrow to go back to the village and build a *simbeck* of bamboo and palm to shelter her."

"You may have a holiday."

"We want to go to the market to buy a piece of cotton cloth and a blanket for her. Among us we have enough money."

"I can give you cloth and a blanket from our school supplies," offered the principal.

"Thank you, sir, but we want to give it ourselves."

"Right," agreed the principal. "You may buy cloth and a blanket in the market. What is your third request?"

"Each of us will go without one meal a week. We have friends who will give up meals with us. We want to carry the food we save to the woman, two of us every morning and two of us every evening."

"I cannot let you skip a meal," the principal said. "You are growing boys and you need your food."

"But the woman needs food more than we do," said Mani.

"You should see how thin and weak she is!" said Sahr.

"I have another plan," said the principal. "I will tell the

cook to put extra rice and yams in the kettle every day and sometimes other vegetables or meat. Carrying it to her daily, two boys in the morning and two in the evening, will be your part. That will be a big gift on days when it is hot or rainy. Six miles over an uneven trail is a long walk."

The next day, the same boys and a few of their friends walked back along the jungle trail. Some had knives for cutting forest branches and palm leaves to weave the walls and roof of the shelter that was called a *simbeck*. One carried cloth and another a blanket. Yomba carried a large pottery bowl full of good rice from the school kitchen.

The poor woman was in a daze at first. It was so long since anyone had been kind to her. She clapped her scarred stumps of arms together in thanks for the rice, which she ate hungrily. She held the new cloth and the new blanket to her cheek, crooning an old song of her tribe. Then she sat there in wonder as her new *simbeck* took shape. It was only a small shelter, not more than five feet long and three feet wide. But it was firmly made and big enough to keep a tiny old woman shaded on hot days and dry on rainy days.

In the late afternoon, the boys left her sitting in her new shelter, wrapped in her new cloth, with her blanket folded neatly beside her, wondering if they meant what they promised. Could she believe that schoolboys would walk six miles twice every day to bring food to a sick old woman?

"May God walk you well!" she called after them, using the farewell of her tribe. "May God walk you well!"

The boys kept their promise. Every morning before school two boys walked from Bunumbu to the *simbeck* by the side of the trail, carrying a bowl of food. And every evening after the last class, two other boys walked the same trail with another bowl of food. They took medicine to the old woman, too, when the doctor who lived twenty miles away visited their school. They knew it was too late to save the fingers and the toes that had been eaten away by leprosy, but they hoped the medicine would make her more comfortable.

A shelter of bamboo and palm does not last forever in a land of rain and insects. After about a year, the boys found that their woman needed a new *simbeck*. This time a crowd of villagers gathered to watch them cut forest branches and palm leaves to build a firm new shelter.

The boys recognized some of their Christian friends and some who never came to the weekly meetings. They recognized also a man who had left the religion of his tribe to become a Muslim. Other villagers came and went, but this man stayed on, watching thoughtfully. At last he spoke.

"It is strange," he said, "to see you boys making this *simbeck*. The woman's own people did not help her. They put her out in the rain. Then you boys came and cared for her."

The Muslim thought more. Then he said something that the boys never forgot. "We Muslims have always said that you Christians do not need to preach to us. We are satisfied with our own religion. But now I know there is something more in your religion. Only Christian boys would have thought of such a plan to help the woman. Only Christian boys would have stuck to their plan."

> —*Alice Geer Kelsey. From "Many Hands in Many Lands."*

NEW WORDS IN THE STORY

Bunumbu	boo-NOOM-boo
Dudu	DOO-doo
Mani	MAH-nee
Sahr	sahr
simbeck	SIHM-behk
Sute	soo-tay
Tomba	TOHM-bah
Yomba	YOHM-bah

Thanks from an Elephant

TICKETY-TOK-TOK-TOK. The sound was faint and very far away, but not too faint for the ears of Maw Kee, playing in the yard of his village home.

"They are coming!" Maw Kee jumped up from his after-school game so fast that tamarind seeds rolled in all directions.

"Who is coming?" The other boys gathered up the seeds, which boys in Burma use for marbles.

"Listen!" said Maw Kee. From far off in the hills that bordered the jungle came a rhythmic tickety-tok-tok-tok, tickety-tok-tok-tok, over and over again.

"Elephant bells!" The boys stuffed the tamarind seeds into the pockets of their gaily colored trousers.

"My father's elephants!" shouted Maw Kee. "The mahouts are bringing them back from the teakwood forests. They'll be in the river camp for the dry months."

"How long?" asked the smallest boy.

"Till the rains come," said Maw Kee. "The streams are dry in the hills now. No food nor water for elephants. They come here to graze in the tall grass by the river. When I'm big, I'm going to be a mahout and train elephants."

Tickety-tok-tok-tok rang the big wooden bells around the elephants' great necks.

"Borus is coming! And Bombo!" Maw Kee shouted.

The boys started running toward the bells.

"Borus is your favorite, isn't he?" asked one of the boys.

"Borus is the most wonderful elephant in the world," puffed Maw Kee, running ahead of the boys. He pitied them because their fathers had nothing but slow and stupid water buffaloes to work in their rice fields. Only Maw Kee could boast a father who was a lumberman with a herd of trained elephants to drag teakwood logs from the jungle to the streams that would float them to the lumberyards when the rains came.

The boys ran out of their village of thatched houses perched on posts. They followed the path that led through the mission compound on the hill. Like the other villagers for miles around, their families knew the missionaries well. They came to the compound when they needed a doctor. The boys and girls who were willing to work at their books went to the mission school. The Christians, and those who were wondering about becoming Christians, worshiped in the small chapel near the hospital.

The boys usually stopped to talk with Dr. West and with the children whose mattresses crowded the hospital porch. They seldom passed with only a greeting.

"What's your hurry?" called the mission doctor.

"Listen!" Maw Kee and his friends slowed to a walk.

Tickety-tok-tok-tok clanged the wooden bells.

The doctor listened. "Elephant bells!" he said. "The dry season is here for sure."

"I love the dry season." Maw Kee forgot his hurry in talking to his friend. "Borus and Bombo and the others will be at the river camp working in the lumberyard of our village. I can see them every day."

"I'm thankful for the dry season, too," said the doctor. He pointed at the roofless porch crowded with sick children on mattresses and blankets. "I have to turn children away in the rainy season."

"You could build another room on your hospital," Maw Kee suggested sensibly.

"With what?" laughed the doctor. "Rooms cost money, and that is something we do not have. Church school children in America have sent money to buy beds for the children's ward, but what good are beds in the rainy season without a roof and walls to protect them?"

The boys felt sorry, but they knew the doctor did not expect them to answer his question. They waved good-by and hurried toward the approaching tickety-tok-tok-tok of the elephants' bells. Soon they were near enough to the herd to hear the crackling of branches as the great animals clumped through the brush. There was trumpeting as though the elephants knew they were near the tall grass and the cool river. One call was louder than the others.

"That is Borus!" said Maw Kee. "He is the biggest of all the tuskers. He is worth as much as three other elephants." Maw Kee remembered that the other boys' fathers owned only sniffing, plodding water buffaloes. He tried not to boast.

Soon the first great gray animal came crashing out of the brush on his broad padded feet, swinging his long trunk in rhythm to the tickety-tok-tok-tok of his wooden bell.

The return of the herd began the happiest time of the year for Maw Kee. Whether the elephants were working in his father's lumberyard or resting in the river camp, he helped the mahouts care for them. All the elephants were smart, but none so smart as Borus. The boy would run his legs tired to bring Borus a treat of sugar cane. He begrudged the time he spent in the little mission school writing on his slate or sharing the few reading books.

One day, as Maw Kee sat on his school bench with the other children, there came a burst of sound that made him drop his slate with a clatter. It was the shrill trumpeting of an elephant. Maw Kee knew what the sound meant. An elephant was challenging another to fight. Perhaps one of his father's elephants had gone suddenly crazy, as elephants sometimes do in the hot season. Or perhaps a wild elephant had come charging from the jungle, itching for a fight with one of the tame elephants.

The trumpeting grew louder. Another elephant voice answered the challenge. Could it be Borus? The voice had the power of the big tusker's call, but Maw Kee had never heard so angry a tone in it before.

The noise turned into the kind of bellowing that could mean only one thing—an elephant fight. Maw Kee had sudden visions of two big elephants, head against head, pushing—pushing—pushing. Perhaps one would reach out with his muscular trunk, twist it around the other's trunk to break it. Perhaps one would push the other down and trample him with his great feet or gore him with his sharp tusks. Maw Kee had seen elephant fights before now. He knew how terrible they could be.

Every child in the schoolroom was chattering questions and jumping up from his bench, trying to look out of the window. The teacher stopped Maw Kee at the door.

"Never go near fighting elephants," she said. "Wait!"

Maw Kee waited—hours, it seemed to him. The bellowing stopped. Maw Kee knew that now the fighters were too busy pushing with their great gray heads to bellow. There were noises aplenty, however—shrill trumpetings of the other elephants milling about in the field near the river, excited shouting in the village, and the loud voices of the mahouts giving orders that were not heeded.

There was a sudden defiant trumpeting and then snorts that gradually grew faint as they faded off into the jungle. The teacher opened the door for the lumberman's son but held the other children back in the schoolroom.

Maw Kee ran on quick bare feet toward the river's edge. He

found his father and the mahouts gathered about a great gray body that was stretched on the ground. As Maw Kee hurried toward them, his eyes scanned the standing elephants. Borus was not with them.

There were signs that there had been a terrific battle. The ground was pawed and gouged. The mahouts' shelter was knocked flat. Elephants were milling about nervously. And there on the ground lay the huge body of Borus.

"Ur-mph. Ur-mph." The groan of the wounded elephant sounded good to Maw Kee. At least, Borus was alive.

Maw Kee pushed his way in front of his father and fell on his knees beside the elephant. He saw blood flowing from a great gash in Borus' side.

"Did a wild elephant throw Borus?" The boy could scarcely believe any animal strong enough to do that.

"Yes, and gored him with his tusk," said the father.

"But Borus put up a fight that tired the wild elephant," said a mahout proudly. "The wild one ran when Bombo charged him."

The story of the fight was not so important as the question of what to do next.

"Borus is hurt!" said the lumberman gloomily. "There's no hope for him! My most valuable animal, too!"

"And my friend!" mourned Maw Kee. "Can't anybody help?" he asked his father.

Maw Kee's father looked at the mahouts, who stared silently at Borus. The mahouts knew all the tricks of elephant care. They could make an elephant obey. They could cure it of small sicknesses or accidents, but closing this great gash was quite another matter. It was too deep.

"Usually they crawl into the river to wash their wounds," said a mahout. "Borus is too weak to walk."

"We must burn salt on the fire," said another. "There's magic in burning salt."

"Magic can't cure. Dr. West said so." Maw Kee's own words gave him an idea. "Perhaps Dr. West could help. Remember how he made the blind farmer see again? Remember how he straightened Aye Maung's crooked leg?"

"But they were not elephants," said his father. "There aren't many elephants in America. The doctor does not know about them."

The boy did not wait for his father to finish. His quick bare feet raced along the slippery mud path that led to the doctor's house. Luckily the doctor was home, and Maw Kee panted his request. The doctor picked up medicines and surgical instruments, and then, because his legs were longer, he beat Maw Kee back to the elephant's side.

Borus' mahout sat on the elephant's neck, stroking him and talking to him. Maw Kee whispered comforting advice into the animal's big ear.

Dr. West set to work. For such a big wound, he had to mix his medicine in a bucket and apply it with gauze wrapped around a big stick. Borus seemed to know that he could trust his friends. He lay still, groaning, while the wound was cleaned and fastened together with many stitches. He moaned "ur-mph, ur-mph" while the doctor painted it with iodine.

In the next few weeks, Maw Kee had two projects. Petting a convalescing elephant was easy. Finding a way to thank Dr. West for saving the life of his big friend was hard. At last he had an idea. His father, who was grateful also, gave him permission to carry it out.

Early one morning a few weeks after the elephant fight, Dr. West heard the tickety-tok-tok-tok of a wooden bell. He heard the soft thud-thud of huge padded feet walking by his hospital window. He put his head out of the window and was greeted by a cheerful grin and a wave from Maw Kee seated high on the neck of his big friend Borus. A big teakwood log was dragging behind the elephant.

Maw Kee gave the signal the mahout had taught him. Borus' trunk shot obediently around the boy and lifted him to the ground. Maw Kee unfastened the log from its chain and showed Borus where to push it with his powerful trunk.

Back and forth between hospital and lumberyard went Borus and Maw Kee. On each trip they brought a big teak-wood log to be added to the neat, growing pile.

By the time the bell called Maw Kee to school, the wise elephant had learned his work. Alone he plodded back and forth from lumberyard to hospital. Each time, he picked up a log at the lumberyard, balanced it on his strong tusks, and held it in place with his supple trunk. He carried it to the hospital and placed it carefully on the pile, nudging it this way and that with his well trained trunk till the ends were even. All day he toiled.

After school, Maw Kee rode Borus again on his trips between lumberyard and hospital. The sick children on the porch sat up in their beds to watch the pile of teakwood logs grow higher and wider. Whenever the doctor had a free minute, he would go outside and figure with paper and pencil the number of logs needed to build the new wing for the children's ward.

"Enough," announced Dr. West as the sun hung low in the sky. His smile included the children on the porch and Maw Kee on his elephant. "We have enough lumber now to build the new children's ward of the hospital."

"If you need more logs," Maw Kee told the doctor, "just tell my father. Borus will bring them."

The very next day the work on the new wing of the hospital was begun. It would be impossible to say who was most excited as the village carpenters sawed and hammered—the sick children who lay on their porch mattresses weaving a wreath of flowers to decorate Borus, or Dr. West who was hoping the new ward would be finished before the rains poured down on

the open porch, or Maw Kee who had thought of the best
possible way for an elephant to thank a missionary doctor.

> —*Alice Geer Kelsey. From "Many Hands
> in Many Lands."*

NEW WORDS IN THE STORY

Aye Maung	eye MOWNG
Bombo	BOHM-boh
Borus	BOH-rus
mahout	muh-HOOT
Maw Kee	maw KEE

Light Pictures

GOOD Minister Chen on this warm spring evening was striding, almost running, through the narrow village street, with his gown flying far out behind. Above all things, Minister Chen did not like to appear excited, or as the Chinese say, "to seem to be boiling inside." For Mr. Chen was a member of the gentry, as well as being the minister of the Christian church in the little fishing village of Mei-hwa, in South China. As a member of the village gentry he read books, wrote poems, had a share in the government, and was highly respected by all the people. A member of the gentry should walk just so, not hurry along as Mr. Chen was now doing. Mr. Chen's father and grandfathers had walked these same cobblestones, with their black cloth shoes toeing out, and their long silk gowns swaying around their ankles.

But then, his grandfathers had never heard of the "light pictures" that were causing all the excitement in Mei-hwa this night.

Last Sunday Mr. Chen had announced that on "week-third" at "down-sun" there would be pictures in the church. Not pictures to hold in the hand, but "light pictures" thrown on a screen at the front of the room, and big enough for all to see. More than that, the pictures would be colored and would show the life of Jesus. Mr. Rinden, the American minister who visited them often in those days before war tore through the land, would bring the pictures.

Mr. Chen's face burned hot to think of how he had urged his church members to come and to bring others. How was he to know that the news of the pictures would spread up the coast to other fishing villages, and down the coast, and back across the rice fields into the hills? Well, it had, and now even before "down-sun," five hundred people had crowded into the village. The church was packed to bursting. Hundreds were waiting to get inside. Two pews had already been broken. Mr. Chen had started his church members singing hymns. Now he was rushing back home to see if Mr. Rinden had come.

"Still not come?" he called as he reached his door. Truly, he did not like to shout like a load carrier, but "boiling inside makes steam outside." Rushing to the back of the house, he found his pleasant, round-faced wife standing over a steaming kettle, which she was stirring with chopsticks. "Still not come?" he said again.

"And if he had, would I be here stirring?" smiled Mrs. Chen. "No, he has not come, but everything is ready—a good kettle of hot water for his feet, and tender yellow noodles with shrimps for his mouth. I wish he would come now, while the food is in its first goodness. After a little—"

"How can you stand there and talk of shrimps when our church is being ruined? There will be no time for resting his feet or for refreshment."

Now it was quiet, happy, little Mrs. Chen's turn to be excited. "Here I have put two eggs into the noodles, and this morning I bargained for half an hour with Old Fish to make him give up his freshest shrimps! And as for his feet," she went on, "I know that you will not let our American friend walk fifteen miles to help us and not offer him the first hospitality—hot water to rest his feet."

"And where in all of Mei-hwa, I ask you, will you find a foot tub big enough for American feet?" Mr. Chen called back over his shoulder as he strode to the front of the house. But Mrs. Chen could hear a smile in his voice, and she went on stirring her kettle.

"*Lai-le, lai-le*. Come already, come already," E-san, one of the church school boys, shouted in at the door a few minutes later. Mr. Chen hurried into the narrow street and through the crowd that had already gathered around the tall, blond American.

"Chen Minister, I didn't know you had so many church members," said Mr. Rinden, with a twinkle of the blue eyes that looked so strange here in Mei-hwa, where everyone's eyes were dark.

"But the church—two pews have been broken—I fear for the windows and doors." Mr. Chen expressed his concern over his pride—the little chapel that his church members had built with the help of friends in America.

If this had been twelve years before, Mr. Rinden might have shown his impatience. But in twelve years of helping churches in China, he had learned from the Chinese that it is better never to "boil inside." Traveling about on river boats and on foot, in times of war, revolution, and bandit raids, he had come up against many difficulties and had learned to be calm when he met them. Even though occasionally a boat had upset and a box of hymnbooks had been drenched, or a typhoon had blown away a church roof, still the Christian churches went on growing. So he looked off over this unexpected crowd and smiled.

And truly if he had said anything just then, he would not have been heard. E-ho, his load carrier, having finished wiping the sweat from his face and neck, and finding himself in the center of so many people, was starting to entertain the crowd. Out of the round bamboo basket he was proudly bringing forth the projector and screen. "*Ai-yoh!* So heavy—bring so far—" He put the long, rolled screen over his shoulder like a gun. "Bandits come, this way do." He made a show of shooting. A hearty laugh went up at the fun. E-ho was a good clown. He could carry on his comedy for some time. Mr. Rinden and Mr. Chen moved into the house.

On the floor, at the edge of the rattan bed, was a foot tub, sending up a welcome of steam. Through the door at the back came Mrs. Chen. In her two hands was a flared, blue, country bowl, piled with a mountain of yellow noodles, and in the side of the mountain stood two red-lacquered chopsticks.

"Don't make a guest of me," said Mr. Rinden, as he bowed and received the bowl in his two hands. "I am one of you."

"You are one of us, and we do not make a guest of you. Rest, eat," said Mrs. Chen.

"Rest, eat," said Mr. Chen, pacing back and forth across the room.

"Is it wise," asked Mr. Rinden, "to show the Bible pictures to so many who do not know the Bible? These pictures were made in Palestine for those who know and love the Bible."

"I am afraid that these crowds will not understand very well," said Mr. Chen thoughtfully, "because so many of them have never heard about Jesus. With such people it is better to begin with pictures of one simple Bible story."

"That is just what I was thinking," agreed Mr. Rinden, as he lifted a mouthful of shrimp between his chopsticks.

"It is pictures these many want," added Chen Minister. "They have never seen 'light pictures.' Some have come two hours' walking, and we cannot disappoint them."

"Fortunately, in my load I have two other sets of colored pictures. One, called 'Beautiful America,' is just for entertainment; the other, called 'Our Foe the Fly,' is to teach village people how to prevent sickness."

"Good, good! Show them both." Mr. Chen fairly shouted his pleasure. "Later on, as our Christian work spreads, we shall show these Bible pictures in all the villages. But the church," he groaned. "Only a few can get in to see."

At this moment E-san came racing in to say that a window in the church had been broken. *"Ai-yoh!"* moaned Mr. Chen.

Quickly Mr. Rinden made a plan. "Chen Minister, while you go to the church, I shall go to that large open square next to the old temple. I shall set up the projector there. The white wall of the temple can be the screen. Everyone can come. Everyone can see. By the time you make the announcement, I shall be ready."

So the ancient temple wall was used for a screen, and to all the people it seemed like magic. On that wall they saw pictures of American mountains and lakes and farms and cities and schools and children with pets. Everyone was pleased. Then the wall turned into a Chinese village where the wise people were getting rid of the flies. The picture was funny and full of good teaching. For two hours Mr. Rinden showed pictures and answered questions. At last, everyone was satisfied and happy and tired. After saying "thank you" many times, they began to drift away.

Suddenly, Mr. Rinden remembered that he had walked fifteen miles that day. He thought with joy of the little room over the church. E-ho would have carried his *pu-gai,* his bed quilt, there. How glad he would be to roll into it! Even on the hard boards of a country bed he would sleep well this night. But where was Mr. Chen? Strange that he hadn't lingered the way he always did to talk things over.

With his flashlight Mr. Rinden found his way to the back of the church and up the stairs that led to his room. When he was halfway up he heard a whisper, "Sh—sh—we are up here." There on the bed he had been thinking about so longingly, ten of the church members were sitting. The rest were on stools they had brought. In the little room there were twenty-three people—men and women, boys and girls.

"Now we want those Bible pictures you promised us," said Mr. Chen.

Mr. Rinden set up the projector and screen, wondering all the time whether he had any voice left to tell the story of the pictures.

On the screen came the first picture. It was the shepherds gathered around their little fire on a hillside in Palestine, as they kept watch over their flocks by night. A bright light was shining down on them. In the light was an angel telling them the good news of the birth of Jesus.

"*Wha-ha! Ai-yoh!* So very beautiful!" were the exclamations of surprise and delight.

Then suddenly Mrs. Liu began to repeat the Bible verses: "And there were shepherds in the same country abiding in the field, and keeping watch by night over their flock." Others joined in. The men and women and boys and girls sitting there loved to recite long passages of the Bible in unison, with a beautiful rhythm-like chanting. Mr. Rinden did not need to say a word.

Next, there was the manger scene with the Wise Men bringing gifts. "And they came into the house and saw the young child with Mary, his mother; . . . and opening their treasures they offered unto him gifts, gold and frankincense and myrrh."

"That's Jesus in the temple," said E-san. There on the screen was the boy Jesus among the old wise men of the temple. "See the old teachers—just like old Ninety-nine." Old Ninety-nine was the oldest scholar in Mei-hwa.

Mr. Rinden could not hurry the pictures because this little group wanted to look and look. How he wished that the American boys and girls who had helped him buy the projector and screen might have been there!

"Just like Mei-hwa," said the men when they saw the fishermen in the boat, with their gnarled hands clutching the coarse brown net. Old Fish leaned forward in the dark to catch every detail of the boat and the fishing net that were used in Jesus' country.

"Jesus said, 'Come ye after me, and I will make you to become fishers of men,'" quoted Mr. Chen.

There was the picture of Jesus teaching from the boat, the blue lake, Jesus in his striped tunic and white turban sitting in the prow of the little boat, and the multitude at the very edge of the water, listening.

"There," exclaimed Mrs. Liu, "I never understood before how Jesus could teach from a boat! Now I know."

"We knew the Bible story; now we can see how it was," said the Christians of the little fishing village of Mei-hwa, as they went to their homes that night.

—Gertrude Jenness Rinden. From "Around
the World with the Bible."

NEW WORDS IN THE STORY

ai-yoh	eye-yoh
Chen	chen
E-ho	EE-hoh
E-san	EE-sahn
lai-le	LYE-leh
Liu	LEE-OO
Mei-hwa	MAY-hwah
pu-gai	POO-guy
wha-ha	wah-hah

The Three Surprises

WHEN Hwei-Lan was a little girl in China, all the boys and girls in her class knew that her father was a candymaker. So one day at school when they were talking over the things they liked best and Hwei-Lan said, "Candy!" everyone laughed. Why! Hwei-Lan could have all the candy she wanted.

The other children told what they liked, and then they asked Miss Lee, their teacher, to tell her favorite.

"Surprises!" said Miss Lee.

The children were pleased. They liked surprises, too.

Hwei-Lan thought to herself, "Some day I'm going to give Miss Lee a surprise."

When school was over that afternoon, the children walked out through the big gate and Hwei-Lan turned and waved at Miss Lee. "Good-by until tomorrow."

On the cobbled street outside the gate Hwei-Lan waved to her friends. Some of them, with coins to spend, stopped beside a candyman, who waited there each day, and bought his colored dragons, birds, flowers, and fans. Others stopped to watch him blow the sugary threads through his special pipe and make pretty figures of candy.

Hwei-Lan did not stop. Already visions of Father's sweets filled her head—yellow dragons, purple fans, pink birds, red all-day suckers, red sugar doughnuts, moon cakes filled with nuts and fruits and baked a crusty brown, squares of sweetened bean paste with cut-up kernels of watermelon seeds on top. What would he be making today?

As Hwei-Lan came near home, delicious whiffs of sweetness floated out to her from Father's shop, which was in the front room of their house.

She peeped inside the shop. Father smiled a welcome as he lifted his big pan from the small stove and carried it to the table. He tilted the pan and poured the shining mixture into a long roll on the table.

Hwei-Lan went closer and watched. She had never seen candy like this. "Oh, Father, it's so pretty. It smells so good. What is it?"

"It's Inch-of-Gold. I've never made it before. See how it shines."

Father patted the shining roll to make it smooth. Then he cut the long roll into bite-size pieces and sprinkled sesame seeds on top of each one. The pieces looked so beautiful and smelled so delicious that Hwei-Lan could hardly wait to taste one.

She reached out her hand for a piece as Father put his long knife blade under one and lifted it from the table. But Father did not give it to her as she expected. Instead, he put it with some other pieces on a tray and directed, "You may take these to Small Brother, to Mother, and to Grandfather."

Hwei-Lan looked quickly and counted the remaining pieces. "One . . . two . . . three . . . four . . . five." Surely those were to be hers! She would eat them when she returned.

The whir of Hwei-Wen's spinning top came from the courtyard. Hwei-Lan watched him make the bright-colored top spin along the string he held. He tossed the top high into the air, then caught it on the string and made it spin again.

"Hwei-Wen!" she called. "It's Inch-of-Gold! It's the prettiest candy Father ever made!"

When Hwei-Wen saw the tray of candy, he put his top down on the ground and ran to her. Hwei-Lan laughed to see him gobble up the shining pieces.

Mother was in the kitchen getting the bean sprouts ready for supper. Hwei-Lan showed her the shining candy. "It's Inch-of-Gold, Mother! It's the prettiest candy Father ever made."

Mother put the bean sprouts on the brick stove to cook. Then she took the tray from Hwei-Lan. "When Grandfather comes from his walk, he and I will have our candy together. Do you like the Inch-of-Gold?"

"I haven't had mine yet," Hwei-Lan confessed. "But it's so pretty I know it must be good."

She hurried back to Father's candy table. The five shining pieces were gone! Could it be that Father had sold her precious candy to a buyer in the shop?

A frown appeared on Hwei-Lan's forehead but before it grew bigger, Father reached across the table and handed her a plate. "This is for you."

When Hwei-Lan saw the five shining pieces safe upon it, she cried out, "I cannot wait another minute!" and popped a piece into her mouth.

Ohhh, ohhh, yummm, yummm, it was even more delicious than she had expected. She looked at the four remaining pieces.

"I'll eat those very slowly," she planned. "I'll make each one last a long time. Tomorrow I'll tell the children at school about the Inch-of-Gold. I'll tell Miss Lee, too."

Then, almost as quickly as Hwei-Lan had popped the first piece into her mouth, she remembered what Miss Lee had said that day at school. "I like surprises."

"I know what I'll do," Hwei-Lan thought. "I'll give Miss Lee some Inch-of-Gold."

She reached for another piece and called to Father, "When you make the Inch-of-Gold again, I want some for Miss Lee. She likes surprises."

But before Hwei-Lan touched the second piece, another thought popped into her head. "If I give her my Inch-of-Gold, she could have the surprise today."

This thought stayed in Hwei-Lan's head and would not go away. Then, so quickly that two of the pieces of candy almost fell off, Hwei-Lan returned the plate to Father. "I want to give Miss Lee the surprise now."

Father brought a sheet of red gift paper from the shelf. He put the four pieces on it and folded it so none would slip out.

Hwei-Lan walked slowly to Miss Lee's house and carefully carried the bright red package in both her hands. Then, holding it in one hand, she lifted the door knocker with the other and sounded the heavy iron ring against its metal back.

As Miss Lee opened the door, Hwei-Lan quickly put both hands beneath the gift and held it up to her. "It's a surprise!"

Miss Lee reached down and took the package. "Why, Hwei-Lan, I thought I would not see you until tomorrow! Please come inside."

Miss Lee carefully unfolded the pretty red paper. "How did you know that candy is my favorite surprise!" she exclaimed.

She led Hwei-Lan out to the courtyard and through the round gate into the garden. "You must have some flowers from my garden to take home. Which do you like best?"

Hwei-Lan went from one to another of the lovely plants and flowers. She looked at the bamboo grove, flowering pink plums, pale yellow and green orchids, orange-colored pomegranates. She bent over and smelled the sweet narcissus with their golden hearts, the spicy jasmine, the golden bells, and yellow jonquils.

"Oh, Miss Lee, it's hard to choose! I think I like best the pink plum blossoms and the little golden bells."

Miss Lee filled Hwei-Lan's arms with the bright flowers. When Hwei-Lan got home, Father's eyes were merry as he reached over and took some of the yellow flowers and tucked them in her braids. He said, "There were two surprises on our street today!"

Hwei-Lan took the flowers into the other room and arranged them in a vase. "They will look pretty in our worship corner beside the picture of Jesus," she thought.

She placed the vase on the low shelf, stepped back, and looked at it proudly.

"When Mother and Grandfather and Hwei-Wen see the flowers, they'll be surprised! That makes three surprises today!"

Hwei-Lan thought to herself, "When you do something nice, it goes on and on from one person to another."

It was something Hwei-Lan remembered all her life.

—*Elizabeth Allstrom. From "The Round Window."*

NEW WORDS IN THE STORY

Hwei-Lan	HWAY-lahn
Hwei-Wen	HWAY-won

The Lights of Christmas

THERE were neither clocks nor calendars in the small village in India where Jaswunt lived. It did not matter much because he did not need them. The sun told him when to get up and when to go to bed. He knew it was spring when he helped Father plant the seeds and autumn when he helped harvest the grain and store it at home in clay jars.

And Jaswunt knew when it was Christmas! Because then he and Father made preparations together for the coming of the Great Day.

As Christmas drew near, Father would say, "It's time now for us to go to the potter's for new clay saucers for the Christmas lights." Later they would go to the market ten miles away and buy silver squares for icing the Christmas cakes, colored paper for Christmas decorations, and powder to make paints for Mother's Christmas pictures.

On the day before the Great Day, the minister, Padre Sahib, would come from the village beyond and meet the children under the mango tree. Father always came, too, and listened with Jaswunt to the story of the Baby Jesus and sang with him the shepherds' song.

But this year as Christmas came closer, things were different. Very different!

Father was not at home, and seven-year-old Jaswunt was

worried. This year after grain harvest, Father had said, "I'm going to the city to find work in the mill."

When Jaswunt asked, "How can I get ready for Christmas without you?" Father had promised, "I'll be home in time. I'll bring money for the hundred Christmas lights. I'll bring money for everything!"

Father had put his bundle on his back and started on the long walk to the market town where he took the train to the distant city.

Now Christmas would soon be here. Jaswunt knew it was time to get ready for it, but Mother said, "We must wait for Father. What can we do when we have no money?"

One morning Jaswunt told his mother, "Ram Singh says his uncle is going to market to sell his new cart wheels. Please let me ride with him."

Mother consented. "If you are careful, you may go."

Before they left, Jaswunt helped to lift the new wheels into the cart. After the oxen were hitched into place, he and Ram Singh's uncle climbed up for their long ride.

At the market Jaswunt helped to unload the wheels and to set them around the stall for buyers to examine. Afterward he wandered from one booth to another. In one he spied the squares of silver and the colored paper and powder to make the paints.

"If only Father were here, we could buy them now," he thought. In his own pocket there was not one anna—only the roasted lentils Mother had put there for his lunch. How could he ever make ready for Christmas all by himself?

Jaswunt found a shady place and ate his lunch. Soon he saw Ram Singh's uncle on the cart. It must be time to start home!

Jaswunt hopped onto the cart. Ram Singh's uncle seemed in no hurry but said, "Hold out your hands." Into Jaswunt's open palms he dropped some coins. "I sold my wheels and made a fair profit. These are for you. You earned them helping me."

Jaswunt looked at the coins a moment and his fingers closed quickly over them.

"Oh, thank you!" he cried, and in a flash he was on his way to the booth where he had seen the colored powder. He handed the coins to the man there. "Please give me as many colors as these will buy! Now my mother can paint the pictures for the Great Day!"

At home, Jaswunt handed the package to Mother. "We do not need to wait for Father. I can plan for Christmas."

That evening a knock came at the gate. Jaswunt rushed to answer it. Perhaps it was Father. But no! Father would walk right in!

Outside stood the son of the village headman. He had a letter for Mother. "The mail carrier came through the village about a week ago and left this for you, but my father has been too busy to send it until now."

Mother told Jaswunt, "Tomorrow you will take the letter to Padre Sahib. He will read it for us and tell us what Father says."

It was early when Jaswunt started across the fields to the minister's home in the village beyond.

"Your letter brings good news," Padre Sahib said after reading it. "Your father is in good health. He will come home the day before the Great Day. He says you are to go ahead with the Christmas plans."

"How long before my father comes?" Jaswunt asked.

"The sun will set twice," Padre Sahib told him.

When Mother heard, she said, "I will begin the Christmas paintings tomorrow. At least, they will be ready."

Jaswunt begged, "Let me try to get the lights, Mother. I'll go to the potter's tomorrow."

At the potter's shop Jaswunt almost sang his words. "One hundred clay saucers for our Christmas lights! Father said one hundred!"

The potter turned angrily from his wheel. "Why do you come so late? The Great Day is almost here. I have much work to do. Where is your money?"

Jaswunt explained, "When my father comes from the city for the Great Day, he will pay you."

The potter was not pleased. "Pay me now," he demanded crossly.

Jaswunt could not speak for disappointment. He turned to leave. The potter suddenly pointed to some chipped and uneven saucers. "Take those. They are of no use to me. You may have them without paying."

Jaswunt lifted the saucers carefully and carried them to his courtyard at home. He found that there were fifty.

Next he went to the oil presser and asked for oil. The oil presser patted his head. "My lad, it would not be Christmas without plenty of oil for your lights. You may have some. Your father will pay. I do not worry."

He put Jaswunt's empty jar under the opening in the press and let oil drip slowly into it.

At home again, Jaswunt put the oil beside the saucers. He hurried to the cotton field. The farmer told him, "Take only as much as you need. Such a small amount I gladly give you."

Jaswunt bent over the white snowballs popping from their thick brown pods and picked a little from one and from another, until he had a double handful of the fluffy fibers.

Jaswunt reached home and found Ram Singh waiting with colored paper sheets. "Your court must have waving pennants," Ram Singh said. He stayed and helped Jaswunt cut the paper into pretty shapes. Together they pasted them to long strings and hung them across the courtyard.

Jaswunt called to Mother, "See! They're waving a welcome to Father."

Mother answered, "The paintings on the floor and walls will welcome him, too."

The boys came and stood beside the white design Mother had made on the ground in front of the door. On the wall there was a star and a manger. They watched as Mother added the pictures of the Wise Men riding on their camels.

The next morning, Jaswunt put on clean white pants. Mother brought her wedding scarf from the tin box in honor of Father's return.

But still Father did not come.

In the afternoon Jaswunt went to the mango tree. He listened to the minister tell the story of the Baby Jesus, and he sang the shepherds' song.

> In the skies on that dark night
> The shepherds saw the shining light
> And found the Babe all wrapped in white.

Still Father did not come.

Toward evening Jaswunt went many times to look out the gate. Each time he told Mother, "Surely Father will be here to help fill the lamps."

When Father did not come, Jaswunt poured the oil into the fifty saucers, rolled the long cotton wicks for them, climbed along the roof, the gate, the courtyard wall, and set the lamps in place ready to light.

At sunset the smoke from many fires cooking the evening meal rose over the village. The lumbering buffaloes, the clumsy cows, the scuffling feet of children, the oxen's bells sounded along the narrow paths and cart tracks. Every creature moved slowly to its home for the night, but Father did not come.

Jaswunt heard the gay voices of Ram Singh and his other friends as they scrambled along the roofs of their houses and on tops of gates and walls to light their many lamps. He could wait no longer. He climbed from wall to roof and lighted his lamps, too.

Again he went to the gate. Again he looked far down the

lighted path. In the distance a tall figure turned into the village from the country road. It was Father!

Jaswunt ran to meet him. "Oh, Father, I'm glad you have come!"

Father's big hand closed tightly around Jaswunt's small one, and together they walked home to Mother.

"There were no carts along the road today to give me a ride, so I walked all the way," Father told them. "When night came, it was hard to follow the path. Suddenly through the darkness I saw the lamps. The lights of Christmas guided me home."

Father looked at all the signs of Christmas. From his bundles he took the silver squares and the money he had promised and a comb for Mother's hair and a new cap for Jaswunt.

Jaswunt smiled at Father. "You are home! Now we are ready for the Great Day!"

> —*Elizabeth Allstrom. From "The Round Window."*

NEW WORDS IN THE STORY

anna	AHN-nah
Jaswunt	JUS-wunt
Padre Sahib	PAH-dray SAH-ib
Ram Singh	RAHM sing

The Church That Was Builded by Moonlight

THERE was rejoicing in the little village of India. The last load of clay had been brought to the trampling ground and mixed with the right amount of straw and water. As the plain around the village turned golden with the rays of the setting sun striking through the dust, the last brick was molded and set to dry.

The small boys of the Christian community played tag among the neat piles of bricks. The women paused on their way from the well to see if the word was true that the last brick had been molded. The young men were checking the count to make sure that there were indeed enough.

Raj Singh, the preacher-teacher, was talking eagerly to the older men. "The ground is bought. The bricks are made. Now in just a few weeks we shall have our place of worship complete!"

It was a very simple place of worship they were planning. Just a floor of beaten earth, with a low brick wall around it to keep out cattle and dogs. The wall would be made with the bricks set wide apart like a lattice to let the stray breezes come through. At one end would be a higher wall rising to a peak.

"That wall we will make solid," said Raj Singh, "and in it

we will leave little openings in the brickwork, so that light will shine through to form the shape of a cross. Thus we shall ever have before us the symbol of our Christian faith. And thus everyone will know that it is a house of Christian praise."

Everyone rejoiced. They hoped to have their place of worship finished by the end of the month.

But there was trouble waiting for them in the village. The Hindu landlord and the priest of the Hindu temple did not want a Christian place of worship in their village.

"These Christians will attract others to their teachings," muttered the priest, "and the worship of our own gods Shiva and Vishnu will be neglected. Let us forbid the building of that place of worship. Then they will not be able to worship their God."

The landlord agreed. He went to Raj Singh and the Christian elders. He did not discuss the matter with them. He simply said, "There will be no Christian place of worship built. It is my order. If any building is done, I will have my young men tear down each night that which is built each day. Save yourselves the trouble."

Alas and alas! All the rejoicing was turned to sorrow. The last-made bricks were neatly piled up with the others, and no one moved a hand to the building. For of what use was it to have the bricks ruined by being hacked down with pickaxes after they had been formed into walls?

Only Raj Singh was thoughtful. "Have patience," he said. "We have a right to our place of worship, and there must be some way by which we can lawfully build it."

Raj Singh went to town and talked to those who knew the law. He found that there was nothing to keep the landlord from destroying their work.

Raj Singh went to another town. The Christian people there were interested. They looked among the laws of the land. They found a law which suited the situation. It said, "If a place of worship is erected and standing, no one may tear it down. But it must be finished before the protection of the law is upon it."

Raj Singh went home. He gathered the Christian elders and told them about that one law. "I do not know how we can protect our place of worship while it is yet building and not finished," he ended sadly.

There was silence for a while. So deep was the thought that the faint rustle of a snake, going about his business in the hedgerow, could be heard. Then an old man spoke.

"There is a way," he said. "But who shall make it succeed? To carry it out, we would need to be more secret than the snake in the grass and more busy than Sher Khan the tiger when he hunts his food and wise as the ant-folk who have a task for each and keep each one working every minute."

"Tell us the plan," begged the elders.

"It is this," said the Old One. "There will come a night when the moon is full and rises after the village is abed. We Christians will put out our lights and seem to go to bed also, but soon we will rise. Silently as the jackal we must slink along in the shadows till the walls of the village are behind us. Then, with the moon to light us, and in silence, we must work. Men and women and children, we must work by the light of the moon."

Raj Singh snapped his fingers in delight. "Wise words! Wise words!" he said. But his voice he kept low, so that no passing villager might hear and tell. "Old One, our planning shall be done with the wisdom of the ant-folk. No person shall be idle but all shall work at one part or another of the brick-work. By the time the moon sinks to its rest and the stars fade out, the building will be done!"

The elders, skilled in the use of bricks, talked long and earnestly. They decided who should tramp down the floor. They planned how the bricks should be carried and laid loosely in place by the women and the children. They agreed that the best builders among them should lay the first course, and afterwards should work on different parts of the wall, each with a group of women and children and older lads to help with bricks and mud plaster.

Like the ant-folk they planned. They thought that the women and the little children might get weary, after the first rush of work was done. So they arranged for some to sit and rest while others worked. But for each there was a task and a place and a time to work.

They did not rush their planning. Best that the village should think they had given it up. Yet with every passing day the plans became more perfect.

One by one the Christians learned about it. But never a word slipped from their lips.

The old Hindu priest and the Hindu landlord laughed to themselves. "They are afraid!" they said. "They have no courage to go forward with their building."

But the moon became fuller and fuller. The night finally arrived when out of a clear sky the moon and a million stars shone down upon earth with a light almost as bright as the sun. Only the shadows were black like velvet, and the Hindu people of the village went early to bed, to be ready to go to a nearby fair at break of day.

When silence lay upon the village, the Christians rose and stole like shadows out into the night. Mothers and fathers and little children; older boys and girls, eager and excited; young men and old; all were ready to work through the night to build their place of worship.

Truly, it was like a colony of the ant-people. Almost in silence, except for whispered questions and answers, the Christians worked.

Almost like magic, that floor of earth, spreading like a pool of water in the moonlight, stretched itself out, under the trampling feet of the workers, till it reached the measured boundary of the wall. Almost like magic, the first course of brick was laid in the four walls around the floor.

Then the walls began to rise, slowly but surely, while the blazing stars swung overhead, and the moon rode the heavens from east to west.

The little children grew weary and slept upon the blankets their mothers had laid along the edge of the field. The older boys and girls grew tired, but they worked doggedly on. The mothers took turns, guarding the babies for a while and then working. They carried water to the men-folk and helped through the breathless, hot night.

One man finished his work, and straightening, stretched his arms toward the stars. Another and another followed. They gathered about the west wall, where the cross had been made, with openwork in the brick. At last only one man worked on, laying the bricks in the peak of the wall.

The light of the lowering moon shone through the cross, and its pattern lay in light amid the black shadows on the new tramped floor.

Then the people gathered into their place of worship, and sat in orderly rows upon the still-damp earth. The mothers carried the sleeping little ones that later they, too, might say, "We were there."

Raj Singh lifted up his arms and the heads of the people bowed in prayer. They did not notice that dawn, swift tropical dawn, had come and that the astonished Hindus stood at the edge of the field.

Raj Singh lifted up his voice. He prayed the first prayer in the new house of worship. He prayed earnestly and mightily and with great love for God.

Then he turned to see the landlord and the Hindu priest, who said, "What have you done?"

Raj Singh answered simply, "We have built a house of worship for our God." He looked the landlord straight in the eye.

The landlord shrugged his shoulder. "I was fearful," he said, "of just one thing. I was afraid you might find out about that law. Even so, no idea came into my head that you might so greatly desire a house of God that you would work thus all night."

The landlord looked at the trodden floor and the latticed walls and the cross in the western wall. "Be secure," he said. "Be secure in your house of worship." He raised his voice. "The hand of no man shall be lifted to move one brick from the wall, or to injure in any way this house of worship. It is the law," said the landlord.

The Christian folk raised a shout of joy. They were weary and their eyelids drooped with need of sleep. But their hearts were light and their hearts were proud. They had a house of worship, where they and their children might gather together to sing the praises of God and to learn better how to follow his ways.

> —*Grace W. McGavran. From "We Gather Together."*

NEW WORDS IN THE STORY

Raj Singh	rahj sing
Sher Khan	sher kahn
Shiva	SHEE-va
Vishnu	VISH-noo

The Mischief Maker

IN IRAN all little boys are important. Mohammed Ali's family thought he was very important.

Mohammed Ali was two years old. He was one of the most mischievous boys in all Iran. His sister Parvaneh, who was six, loved him dearly. So did Mother and Father and Grandfather.

Mother said, "Mohammed Ali gets into so much mischief I'm afraid something will happen to him."

Grandfather said, "He needs all of us to take care of him. We must watch him every minute."

Parvaneh said, "I will watch him."

From the time the family woke up in the morning and came down from the flat roof of their small house until they climbed the steps at night and unrolled their mats for sleep again, they never let Mohammed Ali out of their sight.

Every morning when Mohammed Ali jumped up from his mat, Parvaneh had his clothes all ready and waiting for him.

Every morning Mohammed Ali tried to play tricks. He would stand on his head while Parvaneh pulled his loose black bloomers over his legs and fitted them tightly around his ankles. He would reach in the wrong direction when she tried to put on his white blouse and short brown jacket.

When Parvaneh said, "Now we will wash ourselves," he

ran ahead of her down the steps to the small pool in the courtyard. Several times he almost fell in. Once he did.

When she called, "Mother, Mohammed Ali is ready for you to comb his hair," he wiggled so much that Mother could hardly use the big wooden comb. She had trouble tying the round blue bead on his hair. Mother believed that the bead brought good luck; it was important to wear it every day.

Once when Mother turned the small handle on the brass samovar to fill the glasses with hot tea, Mohammed Ali touched it and burned his hand.

At times like these, Father lost his patience. He spoke sternly to Mohammed Ali. "If you should really hurt yourself, what would we do?"

On the days when Mother told Parvaneh, "I need you to bring drinking water from the spring," or "Please spread the apricots on the roof to dry," Parvaneh could not watch Mohammed Ali. He went with Father and Grandfather.

When Mother said, "I do not need you," Parvaneh took her brother by the hand and they went to the far edge of the village and played under the shady mulberry trees in front of the mission yard.

"The houses are where the missionaries live," she told Mohammed Ali. "The hospital and the church are where they work."

Every day when Parvaneh and Mohammed Ali played under the trees, they saw sick people go across the mission yard to the hospital door. Parvaneh always felt glad when the sick ones came back looking happier.

Parvaneh knew some of the sick people. She knew Ferdose's mother because Ferdose was her friend. The day Ferdose and her mother came through the gate from the hospital, Ferdose told Parvaneh, "The missionary doctor used a big machine and looked inside my mother's arm. Then he knew how to make it well."

Ferdose went to the Christian church in the mission yard. On Sundays when Parvaneh and Mohammed Ali played under the trees, they heard the church bell ring and saw her go inside for worship. On other days they watched her come from the church with teachers and children and play games in the yard.

Ferdose often talked to Parvaneh about the church and begged her to come. "The teachers are friendly," she said. "They tell us stories and teach us songs. Mohammed Ali could come, too."

Parvaneh wanted to go, but when she asked Father, he said, "I must talk to Grandfather."

Grandfather's answer was, "Their church is different from ours. The people are different from us. We are Muslims. They are Christians. No good can come to us from them."

Father told Parvaneh, "No, you cannot go."

Parvaneh and Mohammed Ali went no more to the trees by the mission yard. Instead, they played in their own courtyard. Parvaneh understood. She knew Christian churches and Muslim mosques were different. In the mosque, where Father and Grandfather went, a man on a high tower called the people to prayers. Long before Parvaneh and Mohammed Ali were awake, his call sounded every morning over the village.

> God is great, God is great,
> There is no God but Allah . . . .
> Come and pray.
> Prayer is better than sleep.

When Father and Grandfather heard the call, they came down from the roof, washed in the pool, unrolled their prayer rugs, kneeled on them, and bowed their heads to the ground three times.

One day Mother took Parvaneh and Mohammed Ali to the bazaar.

When the beet-seller passed, Mother paid him a coin for two hot slices of beets. Mohammed Ali reached for the biggest slice and dripped the red juice over the front of his clean suit. He ate his slice in big bites and did not chew them.

Mother scolded, "Mohammed Ali, you eat too fast."

On the way home Mohammed Ali was sick. Very sick! Mother put him to bed and stayed beside him.

Grandfather felt his hot face and brought him a drink of cool water. Mohammed Ali did not want it.

Mohammed Ali did not sleep that night. No one in the family slept. All night they worried about him. But rest and care helped to make Mohammed Ali well again, and by the next afternoon he was as lively as ever. Parvaneh played with him as usual and watched over him.

When night came and the family went to their mats on the roof, Mother said, "Tonight Mohammed Ali will sleep soundly, and we can rest."

But that night while they slept, Mohammed Ali awakened. He got up from his mat. He walked past Mother's feet and Father's feet. No one woke up to watch him. He walked to the edge. He leaned farther and farther. He screamed. Then there was a thump.

Mohammed Ali had fallen into the courtyard below!

Mother heard the scream and wakened. She reached out to the mat beside her. It was empty. She got up and ran here and there but could not find Mohammed Ali.

She went to the edge of the roof and looked over. Then she screamed, waved her hands in the air, and ran down the steps as fast as she could go. Mohammed Ali lay quiet, with one plump leg bent the wrong way.

Mother began to cry out, "His leg is hurt!"

Father, Grandfather, and Parvaneh heard her cries and awoke. They looked over the edge of the roof. They screamed, waved their hands in the air, and ran down the steps.

"What shall we do? What shall we do?" they asked one another as Father and Grandfather carried the little boy into the house.

Grandfather said, "If it is the will of Allah, the leg will be all right."

Mohammed Ali was no longer quiet. He moaned and cried with pain.

Early the next morning Father said, "We must get the bonesetter. I think the bone is broken."

The bonesetter came and stretched the leg. He tried to fit the bones together. The stretching and pulling hurt Mohammed Ali so much he screamed.

Mother said, "I have heard of a medicine woman in the hills. I will send for her."

When the medicine woman came, she put bits of pepper, dried berries, secret mysterious things in a bowl and cooked them into a thick paste and spread it over the hurt leg.

Still Mohammed Ali cried, and he would not eat the good bread and cheese nor drink the hot tea.

Parvaneh sat beside him. She wished she could help him forget the hurting. She thought of their good times in the shade by the mission yard. Wouldn't Mohammed Ali ever be able to run again?

She thought of the sick people who went through the hospital gate and came out looking happier. She remembered Ferdose's mother, and what Ferdose had said!

Parvaneh looked at Mother, Father, and Grandfather. "The missionary doctors can see inside Mohammed Ali's leg. They can make it well! Ferdose told me. Let's take him to the hospital."

Mother said, "I am ready. Let us go now."

Father looked at Grandfather. "The boy's pain grows worse."

Grandfather said, "No good can come from the mission people."

Mohammed Ali cried out again and again. Grandfather lifted him carefully in his arms. "It shall be as you wish."

Parvaneh led the way to the hospital door. Inside, the doctors used the X-ray machine. They saw the broken bone. They told the family, "It is good you waited no longer. Leave your little boy here, and we will make his leg well."

Mother stayed at the hospital with Mohammed Ali. The others visited every day.

When Mohammed Ali left the hospital, his leg was straight and strong again. Happiness came to the family when Mohammed Ali was home once more.

That day Grandfather called Parvaneh to him. "A great blessing has come to us from the hospital in the mission yard. There must be good in the church also. Find your friend Ferdose. You may go with her."

—Elizabeth Allstrom. From "The Round Window."

NEW WORDS IN THE STORY

Allah	ah-LAH
Ferdose	fair-DOSE
Mohammed Ali	moh-HAHM-mahd AH-lee
Parvaneh	pahr-vah-NEH

Two Bright Eyes

KENJI lived in Japan.

Even when he was five years old, before he went to school, Kenji's favorite place was the little garden beside his house. He did not want to go anywhere else.

Each day he enjoyed his white rabbit, the shrubs and rocks, the bit of grass by the wall. He often called for Mother, and she left her work and came to enjoy them with him.

Mother told him, "God's wonders are in your garden."

When Kenji asked, "Will I find the wonders when I go to school?" Mother answered, "God's wonders are everywhere around us."

One spring day Kenji found a curling blade of grass in his garden. He put his finger inside it and called to Mother, "Come and see! I have a pretty green ring."

Mother put aside her needle and thread. The mending could wait, but Kenji's questions could not wait.

"What makes things grow in spring? Will my ring be a tree some day?" he asked.

Mother and Kenji talked together about God's plan for growing things, how life was in each small seed, and how each one grew to be like the plant from which it came.

Mother brought some seeds, and Kenji helped to clear away the ground near the grassy spot. They put the seeds into the ground, and Kenji placed a marker there to measure the first green shoot.

Another day Kenji discovered fresh pink blossoms on a shrub. He called again, "Oh, Mother, come and see!"

Mother put down her knife. She left the vegetables she was chopping.

"What makes the green buds open? Who put the perfume in? Will my flowers last forever?" Kenji asked.

Mother and Kenji saw a bee light on a pink flower and walk inside. They talked about how the bee would change the sweetness in the flower into honey. And how the flower would wilt and die, leaving seeds behind that would bloom another spring. And how God made it so.

A little later Kenji stood on tiptoe in the garden and saw some shining threads of silk swinging gently between two shrubs. "Oh, Mother, come! What's this?"

Mother put down the cloth for wiping the floors. They could wait for cleaning.

She and Kenji watched the swift black spider as she worked. From one high twig to another she carried her silken thread. Back and forth, up and down, she wove her wheel-shaped web that glistened in the sun.

"How does the spider know how to make a web? Where does she keep the thread? Who tells her how to fasten it so neatly?" he wondered.

Mother and Kenji talked about how God had made all creatures in the world and had given them knowledge.

Kenji asked, "Will there be spider webs and grass rings and bees at school?"

Mother answered, "No, but there will be other things for you to see."

One day in the garden, Kenji looked where he and Mother had planted the seeds. The first green shoot had pushed through the ground.

"Oh, Mother, come!" Kenji ran to meet her, and what he told her was like a poem.

> I looked at the marker I put there,
> My little shoot has grown an inch!
> It breathes in the air facing the sky.
> The blade of green is God's child, too.
> Though so very small,
> It is a living thing!

Mother and Kenji went for a spring walk. They bought red azaleas and brought them home. Mother arranged a pretty bouquet and put it on the alcove shelf.

They went cherry viewing in the fields and parks, and Kenji saw the million blossoms on the trees meet overhead like a white roof.

Kenji sang a spring song.

> Spring has come!   Haru ga kita!
> Spring has come!   Haru ga kita!
> Where has it come?   Doko ni kita?
> On the mountains,   Yama ni kita,
> In the home,   Sato ni kita,
> And in the fields!   No ni mo kita!

So the spring and summer passed, and it was time for Kenji to go to school.

On the first day when lessons were over and Kenji came home, he hurried to the kitchen and stood in front of Mother. "I do not like my school. There are no wonders. There's no garden, no seeds, no rabbit. I saw only desks and books."

Mother left the stove. She took Kenji's hand, and they went into the other room and sat on the cushions beside the low table.

"Kenji Chan, dear little son, God has given you two eyes. Yours are bright and quick. Use them wherever you are. You will find the wonders."

In the days that followed, Kenji used his bright eyes and told Mother what he found.

"On my way to school I looked up, Mother. One white cloud looked like my rabbit. It's wonderful the way the white clouds hurry!"

"I looked out, Mother, out of the window by my desk. A breeze made the leaves dance. It's wonderful that green leaves know how to change to red and yellow."

"I looked beside me, Mother. A little boy was there. He shared his ball and played a game with me. We had fun together. It's wonderful to have a friend."

But Kenji still missed his garden. He still liked the days when he could stay at home and play in it.

And then one day when lessons at school were finished, his little feet in their canvas shoes flew swiftly along the homeward path. Up the winding hill, through the latticed gate, and across the porch they carried him.

Kenji could not get home fast enough.

He pushed aside the sliding door and heard the bell ring overhead, but he did not call out a greeting as usual, "I have returned!"

Before Mother could say, "Welcome home, Kenji Chan," Kenji's words tumbled out.

"Oh, Mother, I do like school! Today our teacher put a box upon the table. She let me open it and lift out what was inside. It was a microscope. I looked through its glass, and the things I saw were wonderful!"

Kenji named them all—the drop of water, some grains of salt, a hair from his own head, a live frog's foot.

"In the water I saw little hairs swimming around. The teacher said they were animals. I saw them bump into one another and swim away . . .

"The salt was like shining white stones stuck together . . .

"My hair was like a long black stick . . .

"The live frog's foot . . . Mother, please come and see the wonders for yourself."

Mother said, "I'm glad that you have learned to use your two bright eyes and find the wonders everywhere."

—*Elizabeth Allstrom. From "The Round Window."*

NEW WORDS IN THE STORY

Kenji Chan	ken-jee chahn
Haru ga kita	hah-roo gah kee-tah
Doko ni kita	doh-koh nee kee-tah
Yama ni kita	yah-mah nee kee-tah
Sato ni kita	sah-toh nee kee-tah
No ni mo kita	noh nee moh kee-tah

Sadao and the Story Man

IN THE big polished wood cupboard in Sadao's Japanese home, there was a pretty, square, red box. It was Sadao's box, and inside it there were colored crayons and pieces of plain white paper.

Almost every day Sadao pushed back the sliding doors of the cupboard, lifted down the pretty box, and took out his crayons and paper. Almost every day he drew pictures for Mother. Sadao's pictures showed things he saw on the crowded streets as he came from school or went to Grandmother's house or played games with his friends.

One picture showed an old man walking. Balanced across his shoulders was a long bamboo pole with a bowl of goldfish hanging at each end.

Another was of a boy riding his bicycle. Tied on his back was a mirror that flashed sunlight in all directions.

Sadao drew a picture of a peddler, too, pushing his cart of whirling, bright colored pin wheels, and one of an old neighbor woman sunning herself on a stool beside her gate.

The day that Mother saw the picture of the old woman, she said, "Sadao, our neighbor is lonely now. Her son and grandson have moved away. Show your picture to her. It will please her, I am sure."

That very day Sadao took his picture. The old woman

smiled to see it. "Come again," she invited. After that Sadao often stopped at the gate to talk with her.

One day while Sadao and his friends played, they heard a familiar sound.

Clap-clap-clap-clap! Clap-clap-clap-clap!

There, walking toward them, was a Story Man, striking his two wooden blocks together to anounce that his story was about to begin.

"The *kamishibai!* The story show!" cried Sadao.

This Story Man was not the one the children were used to. This was a strange young man, but that did not matter. Marbles and tops were stuffed quickly into pockets, and all ran after the Story Man to see the pictures and to hear the story.

Clap-clap-clap-clap! Clap-clap-clap-clap!

Up the hill and beyond the vegetable market the children followed, their hurrying feet keeping time to the beat of the wooden blocks. There, ahead, in an open shady space stood the young man's bicycle. Mounted behind its seat was the familiar wooden box, its open side making a frame for the Story Man's pictures.

Eagerly the children gathered around. They hoped this story would be as good as those they usually heard.

Now the young man was ready. He slipped a card into the square frame. Sadao and the others read the name of the story show—"The Lonely Traveler." They waited quietly while the young man lifted out the printed card and put in its place the first picture. Then the story began.

"Once upon a time, in a land far, far from here, THIS man started on a long journey. In his box he carried his good *bento,* his lunch. In his bag tied onto his sash he carried his money. He was traveling from one city to another. You could hardly imagine such a city."

It was true. In all his life Sadao had never seen anything like the low, white, flat-roofed buildings in the pictured city.

The buildings he knew had sloping, black-tile roofs. The man in the picture looked strange, too. The cloth over his head was tied with a band and fell loosely over his shoulders. The men Sadao knew did not cover their heads.

Sadao looked closely at the whole scene. He would remember it and draw it for Mother.

Now the second picture was in the frame. Sadao looked closely and listened to every word.

"The traveler left his city and went out into the country. He walked for hours and hours along this lonely road. You could hardly imagine such a road. As he walked, the traveler thought about his business in the next city. He thought about the presents he would buy there for his children—a girl and boy no taller than you."

The Story Man reached out and measured Sadao's height with his hand.

Sadao hardly noticed. His thoughts were on that lonely road. No, he could not imagine it. The streets he knew were crowded with many people—old men carrying heavy loads, old women pushing carts, boys on bicycles. On this road there was no one except the traveler.

Now a third picture appeared in the frame.

"When the traveler got tired, he sat down to rest and to eat his good lunch of flat breadcakes and a small fish."

Sadao remembered his own lunch—the rice and vegetables waiting at home for him. But he could not leave the story show now. He must know what happened to the man on the lonely road.

With the next picture the Story Man's voice became lower and lower, slower and slower, until it was a whisper. "All that afternoon the traveler walked along the lonely road. He met no man, no woman, no child. He saw no house, no tree, only rocks like THESE—big, high rocks. You could hardly imagine such rocks."

A tall boy carrying a sleeping baby on his back crowded in close beside Sadao to miss no word of the story. The baby began to cry. "Shhhh. Be quiet. Be quiet," whispered Sadao.

"Then"—the Story Man went on, his words coming faster and faster, as he put the next picture into place—"all at once, before you could hardly imagine it, THESE robbers leaped out from behind the rocks. They hit the traveler with sticks and knocked him down. They tore off his moneybag. They ran away swiftly and left the poor man hurt and alone."

Sadao scarcely moved.

"Kowai! Kowai! How scary! How scary! What will the poor man do?"

The next picture was put into place. The Story Man's words came slowly again. "The hurt man moaned and moaned. No one heard him. One hour passed. Another hour passed. Then THIS man came by. But he did not stop. He heard the moans, but he hurried by on the other side of the road—like this."

The Story Man turned his back on the children and scurried with rapid little steps all around the bicycle, then came back to his place beside the frame. Sadao was sorry about the hurt man. Surely someone would come to help.

"Then THIS man came by."

Sadao looked at the next picture. This man seemed kinder than the other one. Surely he would stop and help!

"This man also saw the hurt man. He was frightened when he saw him. 'Too bad, too bad,' he murmured, and he, too, hurried past."

Again the Story Man made the rapid little steps around the bicycle and came back to his place. "Then THIS man came."

Sadao wondered, "Will this one help?" But he did not expect to know at once. All the other Story Men he had heard would stop at the most exciting place and hold out their hands for coins before they would go on. But this Story Man was different. He neither stopped nor held out his hand.

"This man was a stranger in that country, and he was riding his donkey along the lonely road going to the city. You could hardly imagine such a donkey."

It was true. Sadao had never seen a donkey. He could not imagine one. Quickly he reached out and touched the long ears of the pictured donkey with his finger.

"In all his journeys this man had never seen a man lying hurt beside the road. He got off his donkey and went to the man and bent over him."

Sadao was glad. "Oh, he is going to help!"

"The kind man opened the bags across his donkey's back. He gave the hurt man a drink of water. He rubbed oil on his bruises and cuts. He told him, 'You must ride on my donkey.' He helped him get on his donkey's back then walked beside him *soro-soro, soro-soro,* slowly, slowly. Step by step they went until. . ."

Now the last picture was in the frame. ". . . until they came to this place, where the man rested for the night. The next morning the stranger took some money from his purse in his belt and said to the innkeeper, 'If it costs more than this, I will pay when I come again.'"

The story was finished; the lonely traveler was safe at last. *"Omoshiroi hanashi!* Good story, good story!" Sadao shouted. Now surely the young man would collect his payment for the entertainment.

But no—the young man only held out a book for all to see. "I learned the story from this Bible book. If you liked it, come on Sunday to the church building across from the temple gate. I will tell you another."

"Yes! Yes!" the children answered, as they quickly scattered in all directions.

Sadao remembered that he was hungry. He must go home. He hurried down the hill, around the corner, past the tea shop, past the old woman on her stool. Finally inside his doorway, he called to Mother, "I'm home now! I saw a new *kamishibai!*"

After lunch, instead of finding his friends to play with, Sadao took out the red box and began to make pictures of the story he had heard. When he finished them, he found Mother and explained them to her.

"This is the traveler."

"And this is the lonely road."

"Here are the robbers."

"The hurt man rode away on this donkey."

Mother said, "You remember well what you saw and heard."

Sadao arranged his pictures in the proper order and placed them in his schoolbag. He slipped it over his shoulder. "I'll go now and show my pictures to our neighbor."

When the old neighbor saw them, she said, "That's an interesting story. I never have heard such a story."

Sadao invited, "Come with me on Sunday. The Story Man will be by the temple gate. You can hear another one."

The neighbor shook her head. "I'm too old to walk so far. You bring the story to me."

"All right," Sadao promised. "I will."

And he did.

—*Elizabeth Allstrom. From "The Singing Secret."*

NEW WORDS IN THE STORY

bento	behn-toh
kamishibai	kah-mee-shee-bye
kowai	koh-vye
omoshiroi hanashi	oh-moh-shee-roy hah-nah-shee
Sadao	sah-dah-oh
soro-soro	soh-roh soh-roh

Bricks and a Dream

IT WAS the gayest time of the year—the fifteen days of the New Year's Festival in January. Like children all over Korea, the boys and girls of a farming village on Tourodo Island in the Taedong River were celebrating.

The air was full of the boys' New Year's kites. They were small square kites, so cleverly built that they needed neither wings nor tails to keep them afloat, so cleverly flown that they soared and dived and fought air battles with one another. Their colors were as bright as the New Year's costumes of the boys who flew them. Only for the big festivals of the year did the boys take off their cotton clothes and put on their silk outfits of green blouses, blue vests, and baggy yellow pants.

The girls also were dressed in their silken New Year's costumes of long full rosy-red skirts and short green jackets with flowing sleeves of many colored stripes. Their special New Year's game was the teeter-totter. One girl sat in the center of a long plank to balance it on its pile of blankets or rags. Two other girls stood on the plank, one at either end. As each one in turn jumped down on her end of the board, the other one bounced high into the air, then landed again on her end to send her companion bouncing up. Sookney Lee, who was slim and lithe for her twelve years, would bounce especially high, but always landed in exactly the right spot.

There was top-spinning, too, and the eating of quantities of sweets made from barley and rice water.

Best of all, was the singing, at least to Sookney, who had a lovely voice. Boys and girls dressed in their rainbow-colored New Year's silks went in a group through the market place or to the houses of farmers who worked the fields surrounding the village. Men who liked their singing would drop coins into the girls' large embroidered silk purses or into the purses that formed the end of each boy's bright sash. The children were sure of gifts when they sang in their most plaintive voices the beautiful and tragic "Song of Arirang," the favorite folk song of Koreans for three centuries.

> Arirang, Arirang, Arari-o!
> Crossing the hills of Arirang,
> There are twelve hills of Arirang
> And now I am crossing the last hill.

People loved to hear that song that had been sung through the long years as men yearned for the freedom of their beautiful Land of the Morning Calm.

Then the children would shift to a lighthearted tune that made their toes dance inside their rice straw sandals. Sometimes Sookney Lee and her friends would sing their church songs, "This Is My Father's World" or "For the Beauty of the Earth." These songs did not mean much to the listeners who followed the religions of shamanism, Buddhism, Confucianism, or Taoism. But the Christians—and these were many—were happy to hear the glad songs of their own faith.

Sookney Lee and the other children of the Tourodo church laughed as they jingled their purses. Other boys and girls were collecting coins to buy sweets or toys or something needed at home, but the Christian children had a special reason for singing. Their coins would go into the slowly growing fund for building a church. They worshiped now in the same three-

room schoolhouse where they went on weekdays to study. They
had seen the brick church at Pyongyang on the mainland and
dreamed of one of their own like it.

"I have collected more coins for the church today than I
earned in six weeks embroidering the cushion." Poksil did not
need to count her money. She could tell by jingling it.

Pokdong shook his sash pocket. "I have more than I made
raising cabbages for the church last summer."

"But we girls must keep on sewing and weaving," said Soopok. "New Year's Festival lasts only fifteen days."

"We boys must keep on gardening," said Soonam. "Father is
giving me more dry land this year to raise soybeans for the
church fund."

"Will there ever be enough money to buy bricks for the new
building?" wondered Wonsil. "Or will we have church in the
schoolhouse till we're as old as Kim Sunsang?"

Sookney Lee, who always thought more than she talked,
started a new song. Her friends joined in the singing. Coins
began to fall into their purses again. This new church meant
more to Sookney Lee than it did to some of the other children.
It was a part of the dream she carried in her heart—the dream
of giving all of her life to the teaching of Christianity.

Soon the fifteen days of the New Year's Festival were over.
The last kite had been released to fly off into the sky. Every
teeter-totter had become an ordinary plank. The bright New
Year's outfits had been packed carefully away to await the next
festival. The children went back to school.

The work of the Korean year began. The men and big
boys fertilized and planted the dry fields. The women and
big girls worked at their sewing, their weaving, their baby-
tending, and the never-ending washing and smoothing of the
white cotton clothes that were the everyday dress of the men
and women of Korea. And the children learned their lessons
in the three-room schoolhouse. In the spring the rice seedlings

were started for transplanting later to the flooded fields. As they worked, the Christians of Tourodo Island continued to save and to sacrifice for the new church. Coin by coin, the fund grew. No one rejoiced more to see it grow than Sookney Lee.

At last there was enough money to order bricks from the mainland. During the sixth and the seventh months, the Christians of Tourodo watched for the flat boats, lying low in the water because of their weight of red-burnt bricks, to come rowing toward them on the Taedong River.

By the eighth month, men and women were weeding knee-deep in the wet rice fields from daybreak till sunset. After school the children helped, too. They knew it was the busiest time of year. Weeds must not choke the fast-growing rice.

One day at recess, Pokdong stopped in the middle of a schoolyard game and stared toward the river.

"Boats are coming!" he shouted. There were many boats on the Taedong River, but there was a special low-lying look to these two.

"See how hard the men pull at their oars!" said Poksil.

"Their load is heavy," said Soonam. "Like bricks!"

The children watched the first flat boat pull up to the landing. Sure enough, it was full of bricks. No strong men rushed out to meet it. They were all in the rice fields. Only Kim Sunsang, who was too old to work, and Kilnam, who was too small for school, were at the boat landing. The children saw the oarsmen moor their boat and look for men to help with the unloading. But the men, as the children knew, were knee-deep in their wet rice paddies, pulling weeds.

"Who will unload the bricks?" Soopok asked the other children. They all stood there wondering the same thing.

"Bricks are not too heavy for us to carry—a few at a time," said Soonam.

"And it's our church," said Sookney.

In the schoolroom the three teachers looked into one another's eyes. They were all having the same idea at the same time, as often happens when Christians are working together.

"It would be worth more than a day with slates and books," the first-and-second-grade teacher said.

"Let's plan so that our work will be orderly," said the third-and-fourth-grade teacher.

"We have two hundred children," reckoned the fifth-and-sixth-grade teacher. "They could form a line from the boat to the church site and pass the bricks from child to child."

The children who had overheard what their teachers were saying told their friends who told others, until all the children knew. They danced about excitedly waiting for orders. It seemed to take the teachers a long time to decide just where each grade should stand and just which route was the shortest between the landing and the church site. At last the orders came, and the children raced to their places.

Two hundred boys and girls and three teachers stretched in a thin line from boat to church lot. The little children stood close together so that they could pass the bricks easily. The middle-sized boys and girls stood farther apart. Each had to stretch and take a few steps as he handed the bricks to the one next in line. The fifth and sixth graders were spread out so that each must run to keep the stream of bricks flowing.

The August sun beat hotly on the shining black hair of the working children. The edges of the bricks were rough enough to bruise small hands. There was an occasional squeal of pain as a brick dropped on toes that were bare or covered only by thin sandals of rice straw.

Someone started singing a song they had learned in the church service on Sundays in their schoolhouse, "Work, for the Night Is Coming." The bricks seemed lighter as they passed along in rhythm with the song. Finally one boat was emptied. Its oarsmen stood at their oars to propel it back to the mainland for another load. By late afternoon the second boat's last bricks were being carried away. Grownups were coming home from their weeding. Mothers were calling their families in for evening rice and barley with good cabbage pickle. There was praise of the children and their pile of bricks. Old Kim Sunsang and small Kilnam strutted about, as proud as though they had managed it all.

"May we work again tomorrow?" asked Sookney Lee, the girl with the dream to work always for her church.

"If more bricks come," answered her teacher.

More bricks did come—the next day and for two days after that. Except for the rest-time at noon when the August sun was directly overhead and very hot, the two hundred children formed their living chain to pass bricks from early morning till it was too dark to see. Hands were scratched and blistered. Muscles were sore. Faces were sunburned. Backs were lame. Whenever it seemed that the next brick would be one too many, someone started a song that put life into them again. Even children who were not Christians enjoyed singing the songs with the strange but stirring Western tunes. There was a special song in the heart of Sookney Lee. This backbreaking labor was only part of her dream.

"May we help some more?" the children asked when the pile of bricks stood red and solid, a promise of the church that would soon rise in that spot.

At first the men of the church answered, "No. You are too young." Then they remembered that the ninth month would soon be there when the rice must be cut, carried home, and threshed. None of the farmers could help the village bricklayers. There might still be work for the boys and girls.

"Let's ask the bricklayers," said the men.

"The small children can wash the bricks," said the bricklayers. "The middle-sized boys and girls can bring us clean bricks in the round bamboo baskets. As the walls grow, the largest boys can carry the bricks up the ladders. Then we bricklayers can spend all our time on work that takes skill."

And so, through long hot days, the boys and girls kept building. Not so many were needed to wash and carry bricks as had worked in the chain of children from boat to church lot. The lazy ones slipped away. The rest took turns.

So much work was done by the children that the grownups agreed on one thing when the church was finished.

"The children must have a big part when we dedicate our beautiful new building," they said.

"Let's have a choir of children," someone suggested. The idea was received with favor.

Later all agreed that the best part of the dedication service was the children's choir, singing with gladness in their voices and joy on their faces "I love thy church, O God."

There was a special shine on the face of Sookney Lee. The music of children's voices raised in joyous praise—this, too, was part of the dream she carried in her heart.

—*Alice Geer Kelsey. From "Many Hands in Many Lands."*

NEW WORDS IN THE STORY

Arari-o	ah-rah-ree-oh
Arirang	ah-ree-rong
Kilnam	kil-nahm
Kim Sunsang	kim sun-sang
Pokdong	pohk-dong
Poksil	pohk-sil
Pyongyang	pee-ong-yang
Sookney Lee	sook-nay lee
Soonam	soo-nahm
Soopok	soo-pohk
Taedong	ta-dong
Tourodo	toh-oo-roh-doh
Wonsil	won-sil

Pablo Helps with the Writing

PABLO sat in the shade beneath his house-on-stilts in the Philippines. How he wished he could help with the writing of the Book! But he was only a boy, and the Señor Missionary had asked for men to do the writing.

Pablo could remember clearly the words that the missionary had spoken in chapel the evening before. "This Book, the Bible, is written in many languages. It can be written in the words you speak, too, if some of you will help me with the writing. I shall need men who can teach me your words. With their help I shall change the English words into your words. Thus we shall do the writing together."

Pablo thought of his older brother, José, who was already grown.

"If I were a man like José, then I could help," he said to himself.

A man like José! That thought gave Pablo an idea. Quickly he jumped up and ran off in search of his brother.

He found him cutting bamboo to build a new ladder to their home. "José," he said, "if you want to help with the writing, I could do your work for you."

"What writing?" José asked.

"The writing that the Señor Missionary told us about last night," Pablo explained. "He wants men to help him. I am not a man. I am only a boy. Could not a boy help to do the work of a man, so the man could do the writing?"

"That is well said," José said kindly. "But the work I do is a man's work and not for a boy like you, Pablo. Soon there will be the planting of the rice—"

"Ho, the planting of the rice," Pablo interrupted, standing as straight and tall as he could. "That is nothing more than sticking the small plants in the mud. I have watched the workers and I know how that is done. The planting of the rice, that I can do."

José said more, but Pablo would not let his idea go. Finally José agreed. "But when my work becomes too heavy for you, then my help with the writing must come to an end," he added.

The next day Pablo began doing the tasks of his older brother so José could help the Señor Missionary. He polished the bamboo floor of their home-on-stilts. But Pablo did not think that was work. It was fun to stand on the banana leaves and skate back and forth across the floor. Pablo did not stop until he was sure the bamboo boards shone as they did when José did the polishing.

"I can do this always," he said, as he skated back and forth. "Even when José is not busy with the writing."

Soon after, Pablo went with his mother to the market, helping her carry her load. There under the hot iron roof of the market place, he waited while she sold the woven pieces of cloth and scarves that she had made. No other pieces seemed quite as fine to Pablo as those that had been made by his own mother.

Then came the time for the planting of rice. Early one morning Pablo went with the other workers to the field. Each time he bent down, he stuck a rice plant in the mud. Each time he stood up, he took a plant from the bunch in his left hand and held it ready for planting.

Pablo joined in the singing of the other workers as he planted to the rhythm of their song.

> Planting rice is never fun;
> Bent from morn till set of sun.
> Cannot stand, cannot sit,
> Cannot rest for a little bit.[1]

Pablo thought planting rice was fun when he started. But as the sun climbed higher in the sky, he began to get tired. His broad straw hat protected him from the heat of the sun, but his back ached from constant stooping. Down, up. Down, up. Down, up. Perhaps he had been wrong when he had boasted to José that he could do the planting of the rice. Down, up. Down, up. Down, up. Should he tell his brother that the work was too heavy for him? No, he decided. He would work on until the writing was finished.

One evening toward the end of the rice planting time José said, "A few more days and our work on one small part of the Book will be finished. Then will come a meeting at the chapel when the writing will be made known."

In the days that followed, Pablo thought much about that meeting. How proud he would be when the people knew that José had helped the Señor Missionary!

At last the day came when the writing was finished. The people in the village met together in the chapel as José had said. It seemed to Pablo that the singing had never been quite so beautiful before. "It is a song of gladness," he thought, "because part of the Book is written in our language."

After the singing, the Señor Missionary showed the part of the Book that had been written. Slowly and clearly he read from it so that all could understand. Then he spoke.

"We have come tonight because a part of a great work is

[1] The music for this song may be found in *The Whole World Singing*, New York, Friendship Press, 1950.

finished. A part of the Bible has been written in your language. The words that I have read tonight are from this new writing. It has been done with the help of men among us. Fidel Miguel, Juan Rodríguez, and José Martínez have met with me day after day to give help in this work."

The Señor Missionary paused a moment and looked at the people before he went on.

"There has been another who helped," he said. "He is Pablo, the younger brother of José. Each day since the work began, Pablo has done many of the tasks of his older brother. Thus José was free to work with us. To Pablo, too, go our thanks that this work has been done."

Another hymn was begun, and Pablo sang as he never had before. He forgot the long days of bending over the rice plants. In his heart was a great happiness. He, too, had helped with the writing.

—Mabel Niedermeyer. From "My Story Book about the Bible."

NEW WORDS IN THE STORY

Fidel Miguel	fee-DELL mee-GHELL
José Martínez	hoh-SAY mar-TEE-nehs
Juan Rodríguez	hwan roh-DREE-gehs
Pablo	PAH-bloh
Señor	say-NYOR

The Independent Hen

ESTER was the first to hear a faint "cheep-cheep" under the house. She climbed down the stairs from her high-raised Philippine home. She peered through the latticework that turned the space under the floor into a night shelter for the goat, pig, and hens that roamed and scavenged for food during the day.

She saw the red-and-black hen sitting on her nest woven of coconut leaves, just as she had been sitting for the past three weeks. Yet there was a different look about her. Ester, who knew her father's ten hens as pets, could see her proud and motherly expression.

"I hear your babies," said Ester through the latticework.

A cluck rumbled in the throat of the mother hen. A muffled cheep came from under her protecting feathers. Ester ran to spread the news. When a family depends for its eggs on ten hens, the hatching of chickens is a big event.

Ester found her mother cleaning a basket of rice. "The eggs are hatching," she said. "I heard a chicken cheep." She stopped her brothers, Pablo and Juan, in their play with a hollow rattan ball, to tell them the news. She followed the sound of a whetstone and found her father sharpening the broad knife called a *bolo*. "The red-and-black hen's chickens are hatching. I was the first to hear them."

"Of course!" laughed her father. "You have been like a mother to that hen while she brooded her eggs. You have earned one of her chickens as a pet."

"To be my very own?" asked Ester.

"Your very own," agreed her father. "Choose any one."

Then Ester went back to watch the little red-and-black hen and her family. She stood patiently, with her nose pressed against the latticework. One after another, the chickens gave her a glimpse of themselves as they ventured out from under the sheltering feathers. It was not till they were running outside with their mother hen that Ester could count them and decide which one would be her pet.

Choosing her chicken was not easy. They were not monotonously alike as chickens in America usually are. One was yellow. Two were black. Three were red and black like the mother hen. One was black with a yellow collar that would turn white later. Ester could not decide which one was prettiest, but she soon knew which one she liked and respected most.

She was ready with an answer to her father's question, "Which chicken do you choose for your own, Ester?"

"The black one with the yellow collar," she answered.

"Why?" asked her father. "It is the smallest."

"I like her because she is so independent," said Ester.

"Independent? That's a large word for a small chick."

"Watch her," said Ester.

The father watched. Six of the chickens fluttered about the mother hen as she scratched for food. The little black chicken with the yellow trimmings did her own hunting and scratching. "So you choose your chicken because it loves independence!" Her father laughed, but he could understand what Ester meant.

Independence was a word Ester had known ever since she learned to talk. First it was independence for her country, the Philippine Islands, that had come only a few years before. She knew that independence for a country meant hard work and trouble, but that it was something to make a nation proud.

Then it was independence for her church, a little Evangelical one, started by missionaries years before. Now the church was trying to pay its way without asking help from abroad. Often she heard the grownups talk about saving and earning to make their church independent.

"We have depended on the gifts of Christians of other lands long enough," they would say. "We Evangelical Christians of the Philippines must grow up and be independent." Like independence for the country, independence for the church meant hard work and worry, but it was something to make the people proud.

So Ester's father understood why she chose the chicken that liked to take care of itself. Ester named her little chicken Dolores.

The chicken soon learned that she was Ester's special pet. Knowing this did not spoil her. Dolores was much too independent for that. She kept on scratching for her own food, but she did like to be carried in Ester's arms.

"I wish I could take you with me," Ester told Dolores on the day when her church school class held a workday to earn money to help make their church independent. "But you would get in the way of the *bolos* and the axes."

Ester gave Dolores a good-by pat and left with the other boys and girls. It was a hard job they had undertaken, and a long one. They had wanted to grow some sort of crop to sell toward the support of their church. Of course, the boys and girls had no land of their own. No one in the church could afford to give them a cleared field to use. But one church member did have a hectare, or two acres, of land that was covered with second-growth forest.

"You may plant on this land if you want to clear it first," he had told them.

"We'll do it," they had agreed, after talking it over with their teacher. And now the time had come to work.

The girls and smaller boys hacked away at the underbrush with broad *bolos*. The teacher and bigger boys chopped down trees with axes. Working only Saturdays, they spent weeks hacking and chopping. The bigger pieces of wood were carted away for firewood. The brush that was not worth carrying home made bright bonfires. When the field was cleared, one member of the church plowed the ground and another gave seed to plant upland rice.

On planting day Ester told Dolores again, "I wish I could take you with me, but you would eat the seed."

All day Ester and her friends worked by threes. Ester worked with her brothers, Pablo and Juan. Pablo walked ahead with a sharp stick, making holes in a long, straight row. Ester walked next, dropping seeds into each hole—never less than five and never more than ten. Juan followed to cover the seeds with soil. With many other groups of three doing the same work, the planting was finished by sundown.

Then for a few weeks the class had a chance to play on Saturdays. But not for long. When the upland rice sprouted, the weeds sprouted with it. Three times during the growing season, the class swarmed over the field to pull weeds out of the rice field.

On those days Ester said, "I can take you with me this time, Dolores. No seeds for you to eat. If you eat weeds, you will be working with us."

Dolores ate a few weeds and scratched the soil as she hunted for food between the rows of upland rice.

"Dolores is helping," the children laughed. "She is hoeing and raking with her sharp claws."

"My independent hen is helping our independent church!" Ester said this as a joke, but as she pulled weeds, she kept thinking that perhaps it was not a joke after all. Perhaps it was a good idea. She would have to talk it over at home. Her family were poor, but they did want an independent church. Ester pulled weeds as she planned and wondered, with Dolores scratching beside her.

At harvest time, Dolores was not invited to the field with the class. "You would get in the way," Ester told her. "Soon you will do other work for our church." Ester whispered the last as a secret shared with her independent hen.

The class sang the folk song of harvest as they cut and threshed their grain.

> My *nipa* hut is very small,
> But the foods that I grow—
> See it houses them all!

Many of them lived in *nipa* houses themselves, so the song was very real to them. Even the children who lived in frame houses were used to having roofs thatched with *nipa*.

Another Philippine folk song helped them through the hard work of carrying the rice from threshing floor to church granary to be stored till the price was right for selling. It was heavy work for boys and girls, but the song helped.

> Lift, lift, lift!
> Together heave and strain.
> We must hand the heavy burdens up
> And lift them down again.

At last the Sunday came when the church was to have its Thanksgiving service for the harvest gifts. Ester was getting ready for church and humming the song her class was to sing to dedicate their rice. Suddenly, she heard something that sent her scurrying down the stairs on the outside of her house.

"Cut-cut-ca-da-cut, cut-cut-ca-da-cut!" came from under the house. Of course, Ester heard that cackle whenever one of their ten hens laid an egg. But this time the call was different. It had the uncertain note of a hen who had just laid her first egg, and it sounded like Dolores.

The girl jumped from the bottom step and peered through the bamboo latticework that fenced in the animals' quarters.

"It is Dolores!" she shouted. The black hen with white collar was stepping down from the nest of woven coconut leaves, looking well pleased with herself. And in the nest was a small speckled egg. Forgetting her starchy Sunday dress, Ester hurried through the bamboo door of the latticework. She stooped to hug the independent hen, then took the warm egg from the nest.

"You smart hen!" said Ester. "How did you know my plan? This egg is just in time for the Thanksgiving festival at the church!"

In church that morning when the boys and girls dedicated a few baskets of rice to represent the crop stored in the church granary, Ester made a special trip to the altar with one small speckled egg. As she put it in an offering basket where other church members had placed eggs, Ester made the promise that had popped into her mind when she had said jokingly, "My independent hen is helping our independent church."

And this was the promise, made in a voice so clear that everyone in the church heard: "Dolores is God's hen. Every Sunday morning, I will bring to church all the eggs she lays during the week."

The minister looked at Ester's parents. So did other church members. Everyone knew there was never too much food in Ester's house. They knew that there was never quite enough money to buy the things that could not be raised on the tiny farm. They wondered if Ester had her parents' permission to give away a hen's lifetime of eggs.

Ester's parents were smiling at their daughter in her starchy white Sunday dress, smiling so hard that they did not notice others were looking at them. After all, they were the ones who had taught Ester that, if a country or a church is to be independent, everyone must do his share—even the children and the hens.

—*Alice Geer Kelsey. From "Many Hands in Many Lands."*

NEW WORDS IN THE STORY

bolo	BOH-loh
Dolores	doh-LOH-rehs
Ester	ehs-TEHR
Juan	hwahn
nipa	NEE-pah
Pablo	PAH-bloh
rattan	ra-TAHN

White Sails and Blue Sea

"ALL ashore that's going ashore!" bawled out the mate of the good ship *Surat*. The passengers on deck said their last goodbys to their friends. The ropes that tied the ship to the dock were tossed free.

Slowly the *Surat* started moving. The space between the vessel and the pier widened foot by foot. They were off!

Richard and Peggy stood beside their parents, watching everything with the deepest interest.

" 'Tis a year you will always remember, Richard and Peggy," said their father solemnly, "the year 1874, when you set sail from England for a new world and a new life."

Slowly the *Surat* moved out from the harbor. A fair wind was blowing and one after the other, the great sails were set. They filled with the following breeze. The prow cut through the waves faster and faster. The ship was on its way to New Zealand.

It was after they were out of sight of land that the captain called the passengers together. He had instructions to give them. He told them of the rules under which they must live on shipboard, and reminded them how the common safety and comfort of all depended upon the actions of each one. Then he said, "There is one thing more. A case was put on deck just before the ship sailed. In it there are three hundred New

Testaments—a gift for the passengers of this ship. Each person will now be given one, as was requested by the donor."

Two tall sailors lugged a chest up to where the captain stood. It had already been opened. The captain passed out the New Testaments. Some of the passengers received them gladly. Others were indifferent. A few were scornful. But none refused a copy.

Their father wrote in Richard's and Peggy's copies, "On board the good ship *Surat,* upon sailing for New Zealand, in the year of our Lord, 1874."

Day followed day. Week followed week. Around the ship rolled the waters of the great Atlantic. On gray days the water and the sky were dull and uninteresting. On clear days the sparkling green and blue of the waves were a delight to behold.

The time came when the ship rounded the southernmost tip of South America. The passengers breathed a sigh of relief when they were beyond those bitter cold and dangerous straits.

Now they were in the vast Pacific. The ship plowed onward from sunset to sunrise and from dawn until dark. There were hot days and cold days, and once a spell of calm weather when the ship lay idle, its sails flopping in the quiet air. The passengers prayed for wind then, and the lookout, high up in the crow's nest, watched anxiously for signs of cloud or wind on the horizon. A sudden storm might swoop upon them, lashing the sea into great waves, and the ship would be in danger.

Weeks went by as the ship moved slowly across the Pacific. Months had passed since the passengers had left England. But they knew that at last they were nearing the end of their journey.

Richard and Peggy and the other children on board were busy with their lessons. Richard's mother and some of the other women had planned for schoolwork to go on all during the trip. The youngsters had been glad enough for something to fill the long, eventless days. They had used their New Testaments for classbooks, and many were the verses and passages that they had learned by heart. All but the very youngest could read almost any part of the New Testament.

"No school tomorrow!" said Peggy. "It's New Year's Day, and Mama has said that we may have a holiday."

The children went to bed that night in great anticipation. Tomorrow was New Year's Day, and it was also the day on which the captain expected to sight land. They could hardly wait. Who would be first to catch sight of the welcoming shores?

But there were some on the ship who weren't waiting to celebrate New Year's Day tomorrow. The sailors had laid by the extra rations of liquor that each had been given daily, according to the customs of those olden times.

"New Year's Eve and time to get drunk," muttered one with a wink. "Let's to it, comrades!"

And get drunk they did—so drunk that the ship, under a stiffening breeze, plunged ahead with its crew lying useless in the forward hold.

The captain and the mate did their best to guide the vessel through the darkness without a lookout. The passengers, frightened, huddled together on the deck, with empty casks for life preservers fastened to the sleeping children.

Rocks were ahead! But the ship sped on!

Crash! The ship struck a reef, but lifted on the next wave and floated over it.

Crash! Again the ship floated free, but water was pouring now into a huge hole in her side.

Crash! This time the ship was fast on a rock, and each wave that followed battered against it.

How they got ashore the passengers never knew. But when morning came, they were all on land. They had lost everything they possessed. But their lives were safe and that mattered most to them. Some few had managed to tie treasured possessions to bits of boards, which had been washed up by the waves and had lodged among the rocks of the New Zealand shore upon which they were cast.

That they had lost their family treasures and books and Bibles and the New Testaments that had been given them when the voyage started, troubled some of the passengers greatly. Such possessions were difficult to replace in this new land. Peggy and Richard remembered with sudden grief their treasured little New Testaments. The first books they had ever owned were lost in the sea.

Their mother comforted them. She put her hand into the deep pocket of her full skirt, such as all the women of those days wore. "When the ship came into danger last night," she said, "I slipped my New Testament into my pocket."

There it lay in her hands, water-soaked, as was all their clothing, but otherwise unharmed.

Richard's father slowly took the precious volume from her. "We can replace other things," he said, "but this is something that no other book could replace."

Richard and Peggy in their wet clothing shivered a bit. "It's a good thing we have one New Testament left," they said soberly. "We can all take turns using it."

Years and years later, when the old days were nearly forgotten, a man who had not even been born on that long-ago morning stood up before an audience. In his hands he held that little worn and water-stained book. He told the people before him the story of the voyage and of the wreck and read to them from the very copy that his grandmother had brought ashore with her on the New Year's morning of 1875.

"Everything else was lost," said Peggy's son. "But when my grandmother saved this little book, she saved the most important thing that the good ship *Surat* carried."

—*Grace W. McGavran. From "Stories of the Book of Books."*

Simmy's Two Homes

SIMMY'S home was on a big island off the coast of Alaska. He lived there with Mother and Father and six-year-old Ben in a little village tucked away at the far end of a cove along the rocky shore.

Simmy's father and many of the men in the village earned their living by fishing for salmon. Each spring they left home on the mailboat that stopped at the island village twice every month to bring mail and supplies and the visiting nurse. Then they joined the fleet of fishing boats and lived on them in faraway waters until the end of the summer. When winter drew near, they came home, bringing the money they had earned.

It was hard work to be a fisherman, to haul in the big nets with thousands of salmon in each catch. When the boats docked at the big canning factories in the harbors, it was hard work to shovel out the fish with pitchforks. It was hard to stay away from home so long.

Simmy planned to be a salmon fisherman just like Father. He wanted to grow up and go off on the mailboat and join the fishing fleet and live on a big boat. Simmy felt old, but he was only eight. He knew he had to wait a few years before he could leave his family and go away to fish.

The year Simmy was nine, things changed at his home. That year the spring began as usual, and the time came for Father to leave. Simmy, Ben, and Mother went to the little wharf to watch him start. Simmy was feeling very old, now that he was nine.

"I'll soon be a man," he said to Father. "I'll look after things while you are away."

"Good," said Father. "I'll depend on you."

As soon as Simmy got home after the boat left, he filled the oilcan in the cooking stove. Next morning he went to the spring for water. That day he also cleaned the lamps, put in kerosene, trimmed the wicks, and washed the chimneys. He helped sweep the floors and went to the store for groceries.

Simmy was very helpful for about a week. Then he began to forget that he was almost a man and taking Father's place. He did not remember to put oil in the lamps and he left the chimneys dirty.

One morning Ben brought his pail and said to Simmy, "Let's go to the spring!"

They had almost reached the spring when Simmy shouted, "Salmon berries!"

The boys dropped their pails and dashed from one bush to another, picking the pretty orange-red berries. Then Simmy remembered the water.

He and Ben hurried back for their pails. While Simmy got the water, Ben gathered more berries. It was noon by the time the boys reached home.

Mother was cooking the dinner. Simmy and Ben washed their berries, stirred sugar and evaporated milk with them, and made *chedok* for dessert. They liked spooning up the juicy pinkness and eating it.

After dinner Mother rested in her chair. "I'm tired," she told Simmy.

Simmy noticed then that the house was clean and tidy. He knew why Mother was tired. He said, "I won't forget to help again."

For several days Simmy stayed at home and helped.

One morning a few weeks before Father was to come home, Mother said, "I'd like some fresh fish."

Simmy put his line and bait into his boat and rowed out into the cove. While he fished he thought, "Father will see I'm getting to be a man. I'm taking good care of Mother and Ben."

Simmy had caught all the fish he needed and was heading his boat toward home when he saw two brown bears come down to the water's edge on the far shore. It was fun to watch the heavy, clumsy creatures bend over the water, scoop up fish in their big front paws, and pop them into their mouths.

Simmy watched for a long time. When he got home, Ben was waiting outside for him.

"Mother's sick!" Ben said anxiously.

Simmy found Mother lying in bed. On the table he saw the packages she had carried from the store.

Each day from then on until Father came home, Mother rested in the mornings and Simmy did the work.

On the day of Father's return, while they waited at the wharf, Mother said, "Don't tell Father I've been sick. I'll be all right."

They watched the little mailboat chug-chug into the cove and tie up at the wharf. The nurse was the first person to get off. Every person in the village was glad to see her. She came to give help to the sick. Today several people were waiting for her.

Simmy kept watching until at last he saw Father step off the boat.

Father tossed Ben onto his shoulder and took Simmy's hand. "You've taken good care of Mother and Ben, I can see. I knew I could depend on you," he said.

That night at supper Father told stories about the fishing boat and the big canning factories. Simmy and Ben did not take their eyes from him.

No one looked at Mother and her pale face. No one noticed her until she quietly slipped in a faint from her chair to the floor.

Father was frightened. So was Simmy.

As Father lifted her to the bed, he directed Simmy, "Run to the wharf. Tell the captain we need the nurse. Bring her with you!"

Simmy ran as fast as he could go, but at the wharf he stopped suddenly.

The boat was gone! The nurse had gone with it!

Father looked worried when he heard. He said, "We'll have to manage by ourselves until the nurse comes again. Tell me, Simmy, was Mother sick while I was away?"

With a rush of words Simmy told Father about Mother's illness and about the times he had forgotten to help. "I guess I'm not grown up after all," he said.

"You have done very well and I am proud of you," Father said. "I'm depending on you to help me until the boat comes back."

They had to wait two weeks before the boat came in again. Father was waiting on the wharf. He brought the nurse home with him. She went at once to Mother.

In a few minutes the nurse came to Father, who was anxiously waiting with Simmy and Ben. "She will get well again, but it may take a long time. She must go to the hospital on the mainland. I can take her today."

So Mother went away on the boat that very day.

In two weeks a letter came from the doctor about her. "She must stay in the hospital for a year if she is to get well," it said.

In the months that followed, Father took care of the house, and Simmy helped as much as he could. They all missed Mother.

With the coming of spring, the salmon season drew near

again. Simmy saw that Father was worried. Who would take care of him and Ben while Father was away?

They could not go fishing with Father. They could not stay at home alone. The neighbors did not have room to keep them. What would Father do?

One day while Father was downtown with Simmy and Ben, they met a friend who had been away on business on the far side of the island. When he heard of Father's trouble, the friend said, "Don't you worry any more. I know where the boys can go."

He told Father about the children's home he had seen in the town on the other side of the island. Church people had sent a friendly man and his wife there to act as father and mother and to make a home for boys and girls who had to leave their own homes for a time.

"You and Ben will have to go there," Father said. "It may be strange and lonely for you at first. You have never been away from home before. But now you'll have two homes."

Father needed to know at once if the home could take care of the boys. So the storekeeper sent a radio message to the big station, and the operator there sent it on to the children's home.

The next day came the reply, "Send boys to us on the next boat."

When the boat chug-chugged into the cove again, all the village came to wave good-by to the boys. Simmy took Ben's hand and walked on board.

The boat had to go around to the other side of the island, so it was a week later that the mother and father of the children's home called a greeting to the two newest members of their family. "Welcome! Welcome to your new home!"

Simmy made the introductions in a grown-up way. "I'm Simmy. This is Ben."

He felt like a man as he followed the friendly couple to

the station wagon and climbed inside. This second home would be a good place to live while Mother got well and Father worked on the salmon boat. Father would not need to worry. Everything was going to be all right.

—*Elizabeth Allstrom. From "The Round Window."*

A NEW WORD IN THE STORY

chedok   chee-duck

A Chance for School

CECE always knew that she was to go to school when she was old enough. Mama talked to her about it almost every day.

"I didn't have much schooling when I was young," Mama said, "but I want it for you and Irene. I want you both to learn to read from books and to grow up to be teachers."

But when Cece was six years old and Irene four, something else happened. Hard times came to their big city in Brazil, and things were different. Cece noticed many changes.

When Mama went to the market, she bought only what the family had to have—rice, beans, and coffee. If Cece asked, "Please buy a new ribbon for me," Mama said, "No. I have no money for ribbons."

When Papa came home at night, he did not laugh any more. If Cece asked, "Please play a game with me," Papa said, "No. I am tired."

And Cece did not start to school.

Finally things were so bad in the city that Papa said, "We must move to a village in the country. I can plant a garden and raise a few chickens. We will have enough to eat."

Cece liked the idea of garden and chickens, but Mama asked, "Is there a school there?"

When Papa said, "Yes, I have heard there is one," Mama, too, seemed happy about moving.

In the country Papa grew beans and corn, potatoes, pumpkins, and bananas. He sold some of them to the village people. He cut down a tree and made small chairs for Cece and Irene. He made others and sold them in the village. There was money then, and Papa bought chickens.

Papa was happy in the country.

Cece helped in the garden and fed the chickens. At other times, she and Irene played in the sunny yard. They found a white kitten and named it Branco.

Cece was happy, too.

But Mama was not happy, and Cece knew it. Mama had not been happy since the day she took Cece to the village school and the schoolmaster had said, "This school is only for boys. Your little girl cannot come."

Almost every day Mama talked to Cece about school. "Cece, I've taught you to count and I've taught you all the words in the spelling book, but I don't know enough to teach you any more. You must go to school."

When Mama talked to Papa about it, Cece heard what she said. "We have saved some money. I think there is enough now for us to go back to the city where there is a school."

Papa only shook his head. "Prices are still high in the city. Work there is hard to find. No, we cannot go back."

Another time Mama said, "Cece is eight years old now. Irene is six. If we can't go back to the city, let's move to another place where there is a school."

Papa said, "No."

But Mama didn't stop talking about a school. She talked so much that Papa finally said, "All right, we will move back to the city."

As soon as he could, Papa made a trip to the city to find a place to live. He searched and searched until he found a small empty house on top of a high hill. It was reached by forty steps cut into the earth.

When Papa came home, Mama asked, "Did you see the school?"

He answered, "No, but there must be one near."

Cece was not sure that she wanted to leave the country. She had never been to school and did not know exactly what one was like. But if it would make Mama happy, she would go.

When moving day came, Cece and Irene, Mama and Papa climbed on to the puffing, smoking train.

Mama carried a basket filled with food. Papa carried the straw sleeping mats tied in a big bundle. "We will be tired and ready for bed."

Irene carried Branco. Cece carried the chair Papa had made for her.

It was raining when the puffing train pulled to its stop in the city. Papa said, "We will walk to our new home."

The forty steps were muddy and slippery. Cece and Irene fell as they climbed. Mama and Papa picked them up again and again. Finally they reached the small house at the top.

The next morning while Cece and Irene slept, Mama went to the neighbors. "Where is the school?" she asked.

Each one looked at Mama in a strange way. None of them knew anything about a school. Each one said, "My children do not go to school."

Mama was disappointed, but she did not give up. She was sure there must be a school somewhere.

Cece didn't care. She told Mama, "I will have fun playing with the children here."

One morning while she was playing, Cece heard a bell ringing far away. She listened. "I think it is a school bell," she told Irene. "I will go and find the school and tell Mama. She will be glad."

Cece followed the sound. She followed it down the forty steps and along the narrow street and around the corner. And then she saw the bell!

It was on top of a small white building, and children were hurrying through the doorway. Cece followed them. "Is this a school?" she asked the lady in the hall. "Mama wants me to go to school."

The lady smiled. "We have stories and songs here, but this is not a day school. It is a church school. You and your family are welcome to come."

Cece went home and returned with Irene. She liked the church school. The next Sunday she brought Papa and Mama. They made friends with people in the church.

Mama talked to the lady. "Do you know of a school? I want Cece and Irene to go to school."

The lady told Mama, "The nearest school is on the other side of the city. We wish there were one closer. The children here need a school."

But the weeks and months passed and there was no school.

One sunny afternoon when Cece and Irene were tired from their games, they sat and rested on a bench beside their doorway. They watched the others play.

Suddenly Cece pointed to the top of the steps. "A beautiful lady!" she cried. Even at a distance Cece saw that the lady's clothes were pretty, and that her dark hair was wavy.

A gentleman walked beside the lady. They stopped to rest after the steep climb, then glanced around, uncertainly.

Cece stared at them. Who could they be? Strangers seldom climbed the forty steps. Hill families seldom had visitors.

The gentleman beckoned to a boy and spoke to him. When the boy pointed to the bench, the game stopped and all the children watched the couple walk in that direction.

"They're coming to our house!" cried Cece. She had never seen such a beautiful lady nor a gentleman with such a friendly smile.

The beautiful lady looked straight at Cece. "You must be Cece!"

The gentleman looked at Irene. "You must be Irene."

Cece nodded and said, "I'll call Mama."

Mama and Papa came outside. The lady told them, "We heard about you from friends at the church. We especially heard about Cece and Irene. We are starting a school soon. We want them to come."

Mama could not believe her ears. "A school! Why do you start a school? Who are you?"

The gentleman explained. "We are missionaries. In our country the people think schools are important. They believe children everywhere should have a chance for school. They have sent us to start one for the children in this neighborhood."

Papa could not believe it. "Where is the school? When does it open?"

The gentleman continued, "Our school begins next week. We will meet in the small house beyond the church. We will get a larger building when we need it. We are sure that many children will want to come."

Cece's eyes were still on the beautiful lady. "When I grow up, can I be a teacher like you?" she asked.

"I expect you will be," was the answer.

After the visitors left, Cece and Irene, Mama and Papa sat on the bench and talked about their good fortune.

The next week when Cece and Irene skipped through the wide-open door of the small house beyond the church, Cece called happily, "We're here!"

They were the first pupils in the new school!

—*Elizabeth Allstrom. From "The Round Window."*

NEW WORDS IN THE STORY

Branco	BRAHNG-koh
Cece	SEE-see
Irene	ee-REH-nee

The Singing Guitar

"FREDERICO! Frederico!"

Frederico lifted his hand from his guitar and listened. What did Lucia want? He had finished all his home tasks before he had come out behind the trees alone to play his guitar. He liked to be here by himself. Here he did not feel shy and unimportant. Up here on the hill where his own house stood, he could look down over the green plain below and see the scattered houses, small and far away. Near the little chapel where he and his family went on Sunday was a clearing made by his father and the other men of the church so that the missionary's plane could land when he came on a visit to this part of Brazil.

"Frederico!"

If he kept very quiet, Lucia might go away, and he could play again.

But her voice came nearer. "Frederico, where are you? Frederico!" His sister came around the trees and saw him.

"Oh, there you are. Why didn't you answer?" asked Lucia crossly. Without waiting for a reply, she went on, "Don't you remember, this is the day the vacation church school is to begin? The missionary's plane may arrive any minute. Come on! Hurry up!"

Frederico shook his head. He did not care much for other

people. Ever since he had been sick as a small child, he liked to be alone. Now he did not want to go down where all the children were gathered, talking and laughing. He wished Lucia would not order him about so much and try to get him to do what she wanted. Just because she was four years older than his eleven and thought she was all grown up was no reason why she should say "Come on" in that tone.

"Oh, don't be foolish," said Lucia. "Why do you want to stay away up here by yourself? Everybody is going to meet the plane."

Frederico stood up. After all, he did want to see the plane. Only once before had the plane landed on the strip, and that was when the missionary, Senhor Borden, had come to hold services and had taken José's sick grandmother away to the hospital. Besides, it was easier to go with Lucia than try to explain how hard it was for him to stand around and joke and talk with the other children. She could not understand because she never felt shy.

"Wait until I put my guitar in the house," he said.

"Oh, don't bother," said Lucia. "It will be all right here. The plane may come any minute."

But Frederico started up the path to the house. "Go along," he said shortly. "I will catch up."

The idea of Lucia's suggesting that he leave his guitar outside! He went into the house and placed it carefully against the wall in the corner. There was no sound anywhere. Everyone must have gone to the air strip. Perhaps Lucia had meant to be kind, even if she was so bossy. After all, she could have gone on and left him. He began to run and caught up with her where the path turned by the pineapple patch.

About fifteen children and a few fathers and mothers were standing in the shade of the chapel. The men were looking at the air strip, and the women were talking.

"Will he really come? Right out of the sky?" asked Ritinha,

a very little girl. She whirled around and around in her excitement.

"Of course," said Sara, her older sister, "right out of the sky, like this." She made a sound like an airplane and ran around with her arms stretched wide. Some of the other small children did the same, and soon all the older boys went swooping down the air strip with the most realistic sounds.

Frederico watched but did not join them. He went closer to the group of women where his mother was. She understood how hard it was for him to play with the other children, and he could talk better with her than with anyone else.

There was a real whirring sound, the children ran off the air strip, and everyone looked up. The plane circled over their heads and came lower. Frederico held his breath as he watched it. Would it be able to land in the right place on the little cleared runway? Yes, there it was, skimming along the ground and stopping at the exact edge. In his excitement, Frederico pushed ahead with the others and watched the passengers climb out. Senhor David, the missionary, he knew; but the others he had never seen. There was a young Brazilian man who waved to the waiting children. The woman must be Senhor David's wife. The last one off the plane was a boy about his own age. All the other boys went nearer, but Frederico hung back. This was near enough.

Senhor David spoke to the men, and two of them went into the plane with him and came out loaded with boxes.

"Things for our vacation school," he heard Lucia saying importantly, as all the children pushed by to help carry loads. Frederico joined them, but there were not enough boxes and packages for all to carry, so he fell back again. Not all the things were for the school because Senhor David and the young man stood sorting them, telling each boy whether to take his load to the chapel or on to the house where the missionary family was to stay.

Frederico watched for a few minutes and then turned back to the plane. He was all alone. He went nearer and nearer until he could have touched the steps that went up into the plane.

"Hello," said a voice beside him.

Frederico jumped, and the boy who had come in the plane laughed.

"I am Peter," he said. "What is your name?"

"Frederico." He said it so low that Peter looked puzzled for a moment.

"Oh, Frederico," he said when he understood it. "There is a box with a basketball and some other play things that must still be in the plane. Want to come in and help me find it?"

Frederico looked at him in astonishment. "Inside?" he asked. "You mean to go inside the plane?" In his excitement, he forgot his shyness, and his voice was almost as loud as Peter's.

Peter laughed. "Sure," he said. "Come on."

Frederico followed him into the plane. "Here is where my father sits and flies the plane. Sometimes I sit here next to him, and sometimes in one of those seats. Now, where is that box?"

"Here is one down by this seat," said Frederico.

"Good, that's it," said Peter. "It looks heavy, so you'll have to help me. Here, I'll go first, backwards down the steps."

Outside half a dozen boys were waiting. Two jumped forward to help, and one nearly took Frederico's end from him, but Peter spoke quickly. "Frederico and I can handle it," he said. "We do not need any help."

Frederico saw Lucia and some of the other girls. He felt very important and hoped that Lucia knew he had been in the plane.

Senhor David looked relieved when he saw the box. "We won't really start school until tomorrow, but we can play a while and have some songs," he said. "Get things unpacked and help Manuel start some games. I must help Mother."

He seemed to be talking to both of them, and Frederico helped Peter open the box. Manuel, the young Brazilian teacher who had come in the plane, took out the baskets for the basket-ball game and called two of the older boys to help him put them up. That would take quite a while.

Peter put a small blue ball into one of his pockets and a brown one into the other. He tossed a red one to Frederico. The other boys and girls crowded around to join the game, but there were so many of them that it took too long for the ball to go around. Peter took the other two balls from his pockets. He tossed the blue one to Lucia, who immediately started a game with the girls.

"Here, you run this one," said Peter to Frederico. "Half of you come over here," and he threw the brown ball to one of the boys.

There wasn't much to do in running the game—just throwing the ball around the group—thought Frederico. He did not shout as much as the others, but he could catch the ball just as well. When Manuel called them all to come for a song, the boy who had the ball tossed it to him. After all, Peter had said for him to run the game. He put the ball back into the box with satisfaction.

Peter's father and mother came and began to talk with the men and women, explaining more of what the vacation school would be about. They went into the chapel, and the boys and girls gathered around Manuel, who began to sing a hymn about God's love and care. Frederico liked the music and the words. They made him feel good inside. He listened carefully and soon was singing. One by one the others joined in Manuel's song.

When the song was over, school ended for the day. Frederico walked back up the hill alone, humming the song to himself.

Lucia was at home, full of all that had happened and what she had seen in the missionary's house.

"Manuel wants me to help with the little children," she said importantly. She did not mention seeing Frederico carry the box. He opened his mouth to say, "I went into the plane," but suddenly it seemed a little thing. Everyone had helped carry boxes, and it was only because he had not been able to push in as fast as the others that he had been left there to help Peter.

The next morning Lucia kept urging him to hurry.

"Go along by yourself," he said crossly. "There is plenty of time." He watched her run down the hill, then came out of the house with his guitar. He wasn't sure he wanted to go to school. There would be verses to say and questions to answer. If he could just sing hymns and listen to the stories, it would be fun. But if he had to talk, vacation school would be worse than Sunday school because Senhor David would be listening. He liked it better here with his music.

Frederico settled back against his favorite tree, which exactly fitted his back, and began to strum. Yes, he could make his music sound something like the song they had sung yesterday. He sang the words softly to himself and then hummed the tune and tried again. This time it was better! He tried again and again until the words and the music fitted together.

"Oh, here you are," said Peter's voice beside him.

Frederico could only stare. He had been so absorbed in his music that he had not heard Peter.

His new friend chuckled. "I wanted to see where you live," he said. "Then I heard the music and came. It must be time for school to start, so we had better hurry. Why don't you bring your guitar? Mother would like to hear it, and you play well."

Frederico opened his mouth to say he wasn't going to school but closed it again. That would sound silly to Peter. Perhaps it was silly. It would be better to take his guitar back to the house, he thought, but Peter had already started down the hill. So he followed him with the guitar.

By this time all the children were gathered, and Manuel was busy dividing them into groups. Peter's mother, Dona Sylvia, stayed with the boys and girls of his age. She was much interested in Frederico's guitar.

"He can play the song we learned yesterday," Peter announced.

"Then he must play for us," said Dona Sylvia.

Before he knew it, Frederico was playing and singing the song he had been practicing.

"That is fine!" Dona Sylvia said. "Perhaps you will play for us every day when we sing."

Frederico nodded his head. He liked to play and sing.

The morning went very quickly. There were pictures to look at and to make. There were stories, and no one asked Frederico any questions. It was fun when they went outside with Manuel for a while and played with the basketball. Once Frederico made the ball go into the basket. He felt proud and happy.

The time he liked best was the music period. The children were taught a new song. When Peter's mother asked him to play the music for it, Frederico shook his head.

"I must practice it more," he said.

In the afternoon he took his guitar out by the tree and practiced the new song over and over, but he did not take his guitar to school the next day. When it came to the singing, he found that all his practice had helped him know the song, and Dona Sylvia was pleased.

"You are a big help with the singing," she said. "Bring your guitar and play for us as soon as you can."

That afternoon at home Frederico practiced on his guitar. Every time he played and sang the hymns, a good feeling came over him. He tried the songs that Lucia was teaching the younger children. While he was playing, Peter came up the hill to listen to him.

"I like it. Bring your guitar tomorrow," Peter said.

"All right," promised Frederico.

But the next day he lost his courage again. "I cannot play

well enough," he said to himself. He started down the hill without his guitar and then stopped as he said, "I promised Peter I'd do it, and he told his mother."

Frederico went back into the house and brought out his guitar. He walked slowly down the hill, wishing he had never agreed to play.

But after the first try, he found that it was easy to play when the others sang.

"It makes everyone sing better," said Dona Sylvia.

Frederico nodded. He had made a discovery. While he was playing and singing, he did not feel shy. He felt happy.

"Can you play the songs the little folks are learning?" asked Manuel, as they finished playing basketball.

"I've practiced them some," answered Frederico.

"Come and try it for us," invited Manuel.

Frederico went inside and explained to Dona Sylvia. "I don't like to miss the story," he said politely, "but Manuel wants me to play for the smaller children."

"Good! I won't tell the story until you come back."

Frederico walked across the yard to the tree where the little children were seated. They had just finished making pictures, and Lucia was helping them put away the crayons. When he began to play and the children sang, he glanced up at her. She was looking at him very proudly.

"That was good," Lucia said when he finished.

"It was an easy song," he replied.

Every day that week Frederico played for his class and for the little children. On Thursday Peter invited him to his house after school was over.

"Tomorrow you will be going," said Frederico sadly, as they walked along.

"Father has a surprise for you," said Peter, looking mysterious.

"He is not as unhappy about leaving me as I am about his

going," thought Frederico, feeling a little hurt. But he forgot that when he came to Peter's house because Senhor David did have a surprise for him. A big one indeed!

"Will you come with us and play your guitar at the next vacation school?" he asked. He smiled at the look on Frederico's face.

"You mean—to go on the plane?" asked Frederico.

"Yes, on the plane," said the missionary.

"And live with us for two whole weeks," said Peter.

"Mother would not let me go in the plane," said Frederico, but Senhor David laughed.

"That is all taken care of. Your mother says you may go if you wish. And you would be a big help with the songs."

Frederico looked across at the silvery plane and was surprised to realize that he wanted to go. He wanted to make music that helped people sing and feel happy and comforted.

—Esma Rideout Booth. From "Bright Pathways."

NEW WORDS IN THE STORY

Dona	DOH-nah
Frederico	freh-deh-REE-koh
José	zhoh-ZEH
Lucia	LOO-see-ah
Manuel	muh-noo-ELL
Ritinha	ree-TEE-nya
Sara	SAH-rah
Senhor	SEE-NYOR

"Fish Give Ink - Tree Give Paper"

"WHICH one are you carving now?" asked Eugenia, as she leaned over her father's shoulder.

James Evans put down his tool and turned the small wooden block so that his daughter could see the Indian symbol that he had carved. It looked like a "v" on its side, a "v" that pointed to the left and opened at the right.

"Let me see. What does it mean?" Eugenia looked at the board hanging above the work bench. Painted on that board were thirty-six black signs that looked like little tents and triangles and upside-down bowls. It was the new picture alphabet that her father had invented for the Cree Indians of the Canadian Northland. There was a symbol for each sound in their language.

James Evans knew the language of the Crees. He had learned it as he sat beside their fires with them in their wigwams, as he traveled up and down their streams with them in their canoes, and as he rode far into their northern woods with them on his dog sled. But James Evans wanted to do more than talk with the Crees. There was something he wanted to write down for them. And since their language had never been written, it had been necessary for him to invent a kind of alphabet. It was that alphabet that was painted on the board above the workbench.

"Oh! I know! This is *pah,*" said Eugenia, when she had matched the sign on the block to one on the board. Hunting quickly among the blocks on the table she chose two more carved symbols. "These three are *Pah-poo-se,* 'Baby.' " She put three others together in a row, saying, "These are *Mah-ne-to.* That is the Indian for 'God.' "

"There's a symbol for each sound the Crees speak," said James Evans.

"It's like a game," said Eugenia. "Picture-writing is fun."

"That's the reason the Indians are pleased with this kind of alphabet. It is something like their own picture-writing. I left one copy of the board in the village, and the men are learning to read it. They say the board talks."

James Evans looked at his little daughter as she stood there in her bodice and long, full skirt, bending over the workbench. Her brown pigtails hung down her back. He was glad that she had discovered a new game. Pioneer days in Canada were lonesome for the little English girl. A hundred years ago North America was still the "new world," and here at Norway House, the trading post of the Hudson's Bay Company on Lake Winnipeg, the snow lay deep. The Indians had gone off to their winter trapping, and Mr. Ross, the company's agent, had shut himself up with his account books.

Suddenly Eugenia stopped making words and, throwing her arms around her father's neck, said, "Oh, Father, I do hope you can make a Bible for the Indians." This was the serious little girl's way of telling her father that she knew he wasn't carving picture-words just for fun or to make a game for her. It was her twelve-year-old way of saying that she knew his greatest hope.

And well she might know his hopes and plans. Two years before she had come with her mother and father on the long, long journey across Canada to Norway House. A little girl could not travel hundreds of miles by lake steamer and hundreds of more miles by canoe in the Canada of long ago without knowing why she did it.

Eugenia knew and loved the whole exciting story of why the Hudson's Bay Company had invited her father, who was a missionary, to work among the Cree Indians. Over the years the Hudson's Bay Company had grown great and powerful, buying furs from the Indians and shipping them to the fine ladies in England. But year by year fewer and fewer Indians had come to the company posts to sell their furs. Quickly the worried officers had sent scouts into the forest to find out why. Word was brought back that the Indians were going southward in search of a book. They had heard that in the wigwams of the southern tribes there was a book that told of *Gitchi Manito,* the Great Spirit.

That book was the Bible, of course. The Indians had wanted the book that would tell them about *Gitchi Manito.* For like all people, they wondered about God and wanted to know more about him.

When the officers of the Hudson's Bay Company had heard that the Indians wanted the Bible, they had been as shocked and surprised as they could be. But they had decided that they must find a way to give the Bible to the Indians, if they wanted them to bring their furs to Norway House to trade. Quickly the company officers had consulted the Wesleyan Missionary Society that already had missionaries at work among the Indian tribes of Canada.

"James Evans is the man," the society had told the company officers. "He gets along well with Indians and learns their language easily. He loves Indians like a brother and has done fine work among the Ojibways. He will teach your Cree Indians the Bible."

Eugenia could remember that day when the letter had come from the Hudson's Bay Company to their Canadian home. She remembered how her mother and father had talked over the invitation and how they had decided to make the difficult trip to Norway House because it was a great "opportunity" to take the Bible to the Cree Indians.

So the family had come on the long, hard journey to Norway House and they had brought the Bible with them. It was an English Bible, of course. The Indians knew little English. They had their own language.

James Evans had felt that they must have the Bible message in their own language. Only so could they really know and understand God's love. And that was why Eugenia's father had been working so hard all these winter days to carve the Indian symbols.

"How will you make a book from the little wooden blocks?" asked Eugenia, who had never seen a printing press.

"Look here," said her father, and he took the V-shaped symbol he had finished and pressed it into some clay on his workbench. When he took it out, there was the mold of the "v" left in the clay.

"Now if I had some lead," said James Evans, "I could melt it and pour it into this little clay mold. When it hardened, it would be lead type. We would brush it with ink, press it on paper, and it would print a letter on the paper. When people print books, they mold letters from metal, put ink on them, and press them on paper to print words.

"You can see that our alphabet and our type blocks are only a beginning, Eugenia," her father went on. "I've still got to find lead for the type, and paper for the books, and a press for printing. Yet I'd like to be able to print at least one book of hymns and Bible verses by spring, when the trappers come for the trading."

"But James, do you think it is wise to count too much on what seems so impossible here in the Canadian winter?" Mrs. Evans got up from her mending by the log fire and looked out on the deep white snow and the forest beyond. "I don't see how you can think of printing a book without anything to do it with—not even any paper and ink!"

"But Father never says 'can't,' " put in Eugenia.

"This ink the Indians made for me of sturgeon's oil and soot is proving very fine," laughed James, as he took up a blunt stick and stirred some black liquid in a saucer. "There are just two things that I cannot make with my own hands— metal for the type, and paper. There is a metal right here at the post that I could use for type, if I could only get permission."

"What is it, James?"

"You know the big chests in which the company ships its tea from England? They are lined with lead. I could melt that lead and make type for my printing press."

"Nonsense, James! Do you think the company would ever let you rip the lining from its precious tea chests?"

"Well, I know they are feeling very happy over our work here. They say the Indians have never been so friendly as they are now."

Just then the door at the far end of the cabin opened, and there stood an Indian boy.

"James Two-Wolves!" cried Eugenia, happy to see someone her own age. "I thought you had gone trapping with the braves."

"Come back," said the Indian boy.

"Take off your coat—I mean your skins."

But James Two-Wolves paid no attention to Eugenia. He was looking at James Evans. James, who knew the Indians so well, asked no questions. The less attention paid him, the sooner the boy would tell why he had come through the snow.

"Want black water," said the Indian boy at last.

"Certainly," said James, as he moved the saucer of ink to the edge of the bench.

"Trappers take talking board far away. Want make new one."

James Evans was glad to hear that the Indians were learning to read even while they trapped.

"So you want to copy the alphabet, James Two-Wolves? Well, here is a fresh board."

But James Two-Wolves did not want a board. Without a word he reached into his skins and brought out a long, smooth sheet of the inner bark of the birch tree. Taking the ink stick in his hand he began to copy the signs that were on the board.

"Paper!" cried James Evans. "Indian paper! Of course! The kind they have always used for picture-writing. That's it! We will print the hymns and verses on birch bark."

"Fish give ink—tree give paper," said James Two-Wolves, without looking up.

"The oak tree will give us a printing press, and the honorable Hudson's Bay Company shall give us the lining of its tea chests. Mother, I'm going over to see Mr. Ross this minute. If I can persuade him to come here to see our alphabet and our type blocks. . . It might be well to serve a cup of tea."

"I will make some griddlecakes," said Eugenia.

She was turning the puffy brown griddlecakes on the big pan in the fireplace when her father returned with Mr. Ross. Mrs. Evans poured tea from her blue English teapot that had traveled so far. The sun, shining over the treetops and across the snow, flooded in through the cabin windows. Somehow, the plan that Mr. Ross had called "preposterous" when he had heard it in his own gloomy house began to seem different here. James Evans showed him the alphabet and the type blocks. If you think that James Two-Wolves had no share in the drama of convincing the company agent, you are mistaken. He went on dipping his stick into the sturgeon oil ink and copying the signs onto the birch bark as though there were not another person in the world. By the time tea was over, Mr. Ross was certain that it was not a "wild scheme" but a craftsman's careful plan. And before he left he was saying, "The linings of the tea chests are yours, Mr. Evans. I will make it right with the company."

James set to work at once to build a press. For the great screw he borrowed the one that the company used to press the lids onto its chests of furs. He mixed clay, putty, chalk, and sand to make the molds of the picture-words. He pressed into these molds the little wooden symbols he had carved. He poured melted lead into the holes made by the symbols. When the lead hardened in the molds, he had his metal type.

James Two-Wolves' mother and grandmother and the other Indian women cut bark from the birch trees and trimmed it to the right size for book pages.

When the snows started to melt, the Indian trappers began to come to the post. Some were in time to see the first page of the first book in the Cree language taken from the press. Among all those who watched in silent awe, James Two-Wolves and Eugenia stood nearest to the press. They saw the smooth white sheets of birch bark laid on the press. Then the great screw was tightened and it pressed the inked type onto the birch bark. Eugenia held her breath as the screw was loosened and the type lifted. There was a page with the verses of a hymn printed in Cree. Some of the Indians could read it as it was passed from hand to hand. Other pages were printed, sixteen in all. The Indian women stitched the birch bark pages into covers of soft deerskin. The book contained hymns and Bible verses, and one hundred copies were made at the first printing.

Now the trappers were coming in great numbers. Down the swollen streams they traveled in their long canoes piled high with beaver skins. They set up their tents, and the days of trading began. The Hudson's Bay Company had the things the Indians wanted—brown sugar (two pounds for a beaver skin), gunpowder (a pound and one-half for a skin), and tobacco and thread and red cloth and blankets and kettles and checkered shirts!

But it was James Evans who had the book they wanted, the book that told them in their own language about *Gitchi Manito,* the Great Spirit, the Father of all men.

—Gertrude Jenness Rinden. From "Around the World with the Bible."

A NEW WORD IN THE STORY

Gitchi Manito   gih-chee MAN-ee-too

The Witch Doctor's Daughter

MECH made no sound as she peered through the fence at the circle of girls sitting on their heels in the sunny yard next to her own, busy with their books and their charts. She did not care if she was seen by the eight girls, who were Mam Indians like herself. It was the animals in the yard that she feared—and Dorothy Jean. The eleven-year-old girl from North America was dressed like the others in the red woven blouse, wrap-around blue skirt, and bright striped shawl of Guatemala. Even though her hair was light and fluffy, it was not Dorothy Jean's looks that frightened Mech. It was her religion.

To Mech, there was one thing worse than being seen by Dorothy Jean and her pets. That would be to have her father, the witch doctor named Lut, discover her watching the Saturday class in the yard of the missionaries of the Rural Center. She knew well enough what he would say.

"You must have nothing to do with those people!" She had heard his warnings so often that she could repeat them word for word. "I do not understand how the mountain god let those foreigners have their farm school next to my house. He will change his mind yet and destroy them. Till then, we must have nothing to do with them—nothing!"

Mech knew all the reasons why her father hated Dorothy

Jean's family. She had heard these many times. "How can a witch doctor make a living with such a family working against him? Sometimes my people go to the man for advice about their wheat and corn crops or their cattle and sheep. They always used to come to me for predictions and miracles. Now when some of them are sick, they go to the foreigner for medicine, or they let him drive them in his car to the hospital in the city. Before he came, they paid me to cure them by burning rooster's blood to the god of the mountain. Now more and more of my people go to the foreigner's church. They are beginning to believe his God is stronger than my magic. We must have nothing to do with those people—nothing."

So, Saturday after Saturday, Mech was as quiet as could be while she peered through the fence at Dorothy Jean and her class of Indian pupils. One day, as the girls passed Mech's house, they spoke to her.

"Come with us and learn to read," they said.

"I am afraid!" Mech answered softly.

"Afraid of what?" the girls asked.

"The evil spirits of the animals belonging to the foreigners." Mech shuddered. "Afraid of the foreigners, too."

"Dorothy Jean is our friend," the girls told her. "We even pat her dog and cat. Nothing happens to us."

"But you are believers in her religion," Mech argued. "That is why you are safe in the foreigners' yard. The evil spirits are dangerous to me because my family has kept the true religion of the Mam tribe."

"What could the animals do to you?" asked the girls.

"An evil spirit might suddenly leave one of the animals and take me—swoosh—to the crater of the volcano of Santa María. I would disappear deep down in the volcano to be a slave of Juan Noc forever." The worried look on Mech's face showed that she believed every word she was saying.

"We are not afraid," repeated the girls. "We like Dorothy Jean, and we are learning to read. Come with us."

"But I am an unbeliever," said Mech.

Mech was thinking over what the girls said, when she met Dorothy Jean's mother on the road near their homes. Mrs. Peck had lived in Guatemala long enough to speak both Spanish and the Mam language well. Like Dorothy Jean, she wore the bright red blouse, blue skirt, and colored shawl of the Indians. She seemed to belong to the country. Her smile invited Mech to speak.

With all her courage, Mech spoke in a small and shaky voice, "Can an unbeliever learn to read?"

"Of course!" Mrs. Peck's smile was warmer than ever. "Come to Dorothy Jean's school next Saturday. She will teach you to read. Bring your brother and sister with you."

Mech ran away without answering, but she did not forget. The next Saturday found her slipping cautiously through the gate into the compound of the Rural Center. She came alone, not taking chances with her small brother and sister.

She found Dorothy Jean with the circle of girls sitting on their heels while they sang together. And there were the animals that Mech feared. Dragging her feet, Mech moved slowly into the yard. A dog frisked about her, wagging his tail. A cat rubbed against her legs, purring. Mech imagined herself whisking through the air to be dropped into the volcano—never to return. As the dog poked a friendly cool nose into her hand, she thought of Juan Noc in the volcano crater waiting to make her his slave. The dog licked her hand. Mech jumped—but nothing happened.

"Come join us, Mech," called Dorothy Jean as the song ended. The girls moved to make room for one more in front of the reading charts. Mech looked about her fearfully. Then she sat down on her small bare heels and stared at the lines and pictures on the mysterious charts.

When Mech went home after class, the witch doctor and his wife Ana were horrified to hear where she had been.

"Do you feel sick?" they asked. "Did the foreigners cast an evil spell on you?" The witch doctor went to his sacred table to match the red beans to see if Mech needed a cure.

"I'm all right," Mech said. "I'm learning to read."

Then began a chain of little events that led to something the witch doctor's daughter would never have dreamed could happen. Every Saturday Mech went to Dorothy Jean's class and came home happy and unharmed. And every Saturday Lut and Ana seemed to hate and fear the foreigners next door a little less. They let their smaller children go to the class with Mech. They began to ask questions of some of the Indians who were believers. Mech liked to stand beside her parents and listen to the questions and the answers.

One day Ana fell sick—very sick. Lut tried every charm that he knew. He went to the hilltop and sacrificed a rooster. Nothing helped. Mech thought he did not seem surprised, as though he knew that his magic was better at making money than at curing people. As her mother grew worse, the girl dared to take a great chance.

"Dorothy Jean's mother has medicines," Mech suggested in a small and timid voice. "Shall I call her?"

The witch doctor knew that his wife was growing worse in spite of his magic.

"Run!" he said to Mech. "Bring her here!"

Mrs. Peck came quickly from next door and helped Ana as much as she could.

"The doctor will be at our clinic tomorrow," she said. "He will know what to do."

Ana was afraid, but she was sick enough to try even the foreigner's cures. When the doctor came to treat her, she was glad to see him. Within a few hours she felt better, and soon she was well again.

After that, Mech's family found it easy to go next door now and then. When no harm came to them, they grew bolder—and more curious. One day they risked going to the adobe chapel where Dorothy Jean's father preached and her mother played a small organ. To their surprise, they liked the singing and could find no fault with what was said. And they were not whisked off suddenly on an air journey to the live volcano's crater.

Lut was smart enough to know the truth about the charms by which he collected ten times as much money as his neighbors earned by hard work. He knew that his magic was a wonderful way to make a living—but a poor way to help people. That his charms were make-believe was his carefully kept secret, shared only with the fifteen other witch doctors of the vicinity. Though he began to see that the Evangelical church taught truth, he hated to give up his good business. Why should he work long hours for a few cents at hard labor in the cornfields nearby or on the banana and coffee plantations of the lowlands, when he could quickly earn money just by matching red beans at his sacred table or praying to a stone idol?

Mech made her decision first. It was at the Christmas service in the little adobe chapel. Men, women, and children were sitting on planks raised a little above the hard-packed ground that made the floor of the chapel. The women and girls were gay in their best blouses, skirts, and bright shawls. Mech loved the story and the songs about the Baby who had grown up to be a leader and a Savior for all who believed in him. She watched neighbors saying for the first time that they wanted to belong to Jesus.

"Who else wishes to belong to Jesus?" asked the minister quietly.

"I!" Mech's voice was small, but her step was firm as she walked to the front of the little chapel.

Again came the question, "Does anyone else wish to belong to Jesus?" There were footsteps behind Mech, and two voices answering, "Yes!"

Mech knew those footsteps—and those voices. She was happy that her parents were becoming believers with her. Lut and Ana sounded happy, too.

But the family of Mech had two hard battles ahead of them.

The first had to do with the tools of the witch doctor's trade. It was one thing for Lut, at a lovely Christmas service, to say "Yes" to a quiet question in a church. It was quite another thing to make up his mind that he would never again practice the trade that earned money so easily.

The sacred table seemed harmless in the corner of Lut's thatched house. It had stood there as long as Mech could remember, covered with the tools of the witch doctor's trade —crosses, red beans, a gourd for the god's drink, and a red velvet flag. Mech was so used to it that she scarcely noticed it was there. At least, she did not notice it till the morning after her father's dream.

"Such a dream I had last night," he said. "It was about a snake coming to me in my own house to tell me I must—"

"Must what?" urged Mech.

"That I must—" He glanced nervously at the sacred table. Then Mech knew.

"Get rid of a witch doctor's tools?" she guessed.

"Yes!" Lut walked slowly toward the sacred table where he had worked his charms until he almost believed them himself.

Perhaps it was the serious eyes of Mech that gave him courage to pick up the four-pronged crosses with their arms reaching to the four points of the compass. Out in the yard he made a bonfire of straw. Mech threw on a few armfuls to make a bigger blaze. Lut did not need to tell her why he was building the fire. Into the center of the fire he threw the crosses and all the charms of a witch doctor's trade. As they burned, he looked back at the table.

"That table is too good to burn," said Ana. "It must leave our house, but someone else might be able to use it as an ordinary table."

"We know it has no magic power," said Lut. "Unbelievers would be afraid of it, but believers would not."

So a few days later, an elder of the church came with his carrying strap. He slung the table on his back and balanced it by the carrying strap around his forehead. Mech watched the table go bobbing out of sight on his back. Then she and her family felt safe from any fear that Lut would ever be tempted to earn money the dishonest and easy way again.

But they had one more battle to fight. The fifteen other witch doctors who lived nearby were as angry as they were frightened at what Lut had done. Like him, they knew that their sacrifices, charms, and dances could never make the crops grow nor cure anyone. It had been all right when all sixteen of them were keeping their secret. But now—

"Lut will tell!" they told one another. "We must frighten him into leaving this new religion and coming back to ours."

They knew they could not frighten him by magic, so they tried threats. Lut's children never knew what would happen to them when they stepped outside their own yard. All kinds of "accidents" happened to the cornfields where Lut was trying to earn his family's living. Ana did not dare take her children with her when she went to the brook to wash the clothes. What one witch doctor did not think of, another would. Fifteen minds were working overtime to make life uncomfortable for the family who could give away their secrets.

But the threats and tricks of fifteen witch doctors were not enough to frighten a family of believers. Lut had burned the tools of the witch doctor's trade forever. Even the fifteen witch doctors finally gave up annoying a family that said and believed, "Our God loves us and will protect us."

> —*Alice Geer Kelsey. From "Many Hands in Many Lands."*

NEW WORDS IN THE STORY

Ana	AH-nah
Juan Noc	hwahn nock
Lut	loot
Mam	mahm
Mech	metch
Santa María	SAHN-tah mah-REE-ah

A Present for Plumita

CHABELA'S home was a small house high on a mountainside in Mexico. Six-year-old Chabela had never traveled farther from home than the foot of the mountain, but she wanted to. She wanted to ride on the train. She wanted to go with Papá to the meeting of church friends. She wanted to see the missionaries about whom Papá talked so much.

Each year when Papá went away for the week's meeting with the Christian leaders, Chabela begged, "Please take me with you."

Each year Papá's answer was always the same—"When you are older."

So Chabela had to be content at home. Sometimes this was hard.

When Chabela tried to play marbles with her two big brothers, they always said, "You are too little to play with us," and then ran off to play by themselves.

When she tried to play "Odds and Evens" with her two little brothers, the game was no fun. The boys had not yet learned about odd numbers and even ones.

But Chabela always had Plumita.

Plumita was a little pet turkey hen that followed Chabela wherever she went—into the house to watch Mamá make Chabela's new red dress, onto the step to hear Chabela spell words from her schoolbook, into the patio to wait for Papá to come on the burro from the field down the mountain, beside the fence to listen to the train whistle sounding up from the valley . . . ʊʊʊʊʊʊ ʊʊʊʊʊʊ ʊʊ ʊʊ!

Every day Chabela talked to Plumita.

"This morning I helped Mamá make *tortillas,* good corn-meal pancakes. Here's some *masa,* corn dough, for you!"

"Look at this pretty round stone."

"I picked this flower down near the spring."

Plumita always seemed to understand.

One morning there was exciting news to tell, and Chabela hurried into the yard. She threw out a few grains of corn and wheat and called, "Plumita! Plumita! I have something to tell you." But her little pet did not come.

Where could she be?

Chabela looked for her under the step. She looked for her behind the broken water jar and under the old basket. She looked for her out beyond the pile of corn fodder. Plumita was not in any of those places.

Back in the house Chabela looked for Plumita under her very own bed. And there she was! On a nest!

"Plumita, are you hatching eggs?" Chabela asked. She reached over and slipped her hand under Plumita's brown feathers and counted the hidden eggs. "One, two, three, four. Oh, Plumita, must you hatch them now?"

Plumita made no answer. Chabela continued with her news. "I'm old enough now! Papá says I may go to the meeting. Papá says all the family may go. I wanted you to go!"

Plumita only blinked.

In the days that followed, Chabela heard Mamá and Papá talk over plans for seeing again the missionary friends who already had helped them in so many ways. She told Plumita what she heard.

"The yellow corn I bring you every day, Plumita, the missionary says is better for you and for our family than the white corn we used to have."

"The little tree in the yard, Plumita, Papá bought from the missionary. Soon red apples will grow on it."

"This picture of Jesus, Plumita, the missionary sent to me for a present."

"Plumita, when you hear the whistle tomorrow, ʊʊʊʊʊʊ ʊʊʊʊʊʊ ʊʊ ʊʊ, I'll be on the train."

When tomorrow came, Chabela's two big brothers rolled up the seven blankets ready to carry on their backs. The family would need them for sleeping.

Her two little brothers helped Papá pour out the beans from the big jar into a strong bag for him to carry. They would be payment for the family's food and room while they were away.

Chabela, wearing her new red dress, helped to pack cold boiled meat, *tortillas,* and chili in the *tenate,* the woven string bag that Mamá would carry on her back. The food would taste good on the hot, dusty train ride.

When the family and bundles were ready, Chabela reached under the bed and gave Plumita a final loving pat. "You won't be lonesome," she promised. *"Abuelita,* Little Grandmother, from next door, will come every day and feed you. I'll soon be back, and I'll bring you a present from the missionary! *Adiós."*

On the trip to the train stop, Mamá, Papá, and the two big brothers walked the long distance, slipping and sliding down the steep path.

Chabela and the two little brothers rode on the burro's back. The burro would remain in Cousin Pedro's stable in the village to be ready to carry the children home again.

At the station when the train finally came to its puffing, jolting stop, Chabela could hardly believe what she saw. Why, each of the two cars was larger than her house! From the mountain top the cars and engine had looked so small, winding their way along the river. Often she could not even see them until the black curling smoke or the ʊʊʊʊʊʊ ʊʊʊʊʊʊ ʊʊ ʊʊ of the whistle helped her to find them.

The benches in the front car seemed very hard to Chabela as she sat on one of them. But when she complained to Papá, he said, "This car gets us there as soon as the soft-seated car behind us, and it costs not so much. So here we stay."

The train crossed and recrossed the winding river. It went through dark tunnels and past trees covered with pretty colorful orchids. To Chabela, the best part of the ride was when the train stopped and Papá reached through a window and from a boy on the platform bought *limonada* and juicy fruits for the family to enjoy.

By evening when they left the train and joined the other visiting families, everyone was tired. Soon, wrapped in their blankets, fathers, mothers, and children were asleep on the floor of the big room prepared for them near the church.

The next morning, over fires built in a shady patio Mamá and other women cooked beans and *tortillas* for breakfast. Then everyone went to the meeting in the church.

That morning in one of the church rooms Chabela stopped at a long table. On it were colored pictures like the ones the missionary had sent home to her. Chabela stopped and looked at them and listened to the missionary teacher tell Bible stories. Maybe Plumita would like a Bible picture!

The next day in the church yard, Chabela discovered the missionary's station wagon. She stood on tiptoe and looked inside. She might see something there for Plumita! There were little trees, more than she could count, each in a small paper box. And there were bags of meal and bran. But Plumita already had enough food to eat, and she certainly wouldn't want a tree.

Just then a friendly voice called, *"Buenos días,* good morning. May I help you?" Chabela saw one of the missionaries smiling at her.

"I want something for Plumita," Chabela explained. "I promised I'd bring her a present." She told the missionary about her pet and the nest under the bed.

The missionary lifted out a box and opened the lid, and Chabela looked inside. "How about a few of these eggs for your pet?" he said. "She might break one of hers, or a rat might eat one. These eggs will hatch into fine chickens."

That night Chabela asked Mamá and Papá about taking eggs to Plumita. Mamá said, "Eggs will break in the *tenate*. I cannot carry them safely on the train and up the mountain."

Papá said, "Plumita's eggs will be hatched by the time we get home. I think it will be best if you find another present for her."

The next day and the next Chabela tried, but nothing that she saw seemed right. Then on the day before the meeting closed, Chabela again passed the station wagon. This time she heard sounds coming from inside.

Chirrup, chirrup, chirrup, chirrup!

The missionary called to Chabela. "How about these for Plumita?" Into her hands he put some fluffy baby chickens, just hatched. "Slip these into the nest with Plumita's little turkeys. She will care for them. When they grow up, they will lay many fine eggs for you."

"Oh!" cried Chabela, holding the soft chirruping chickens. "This present won't break in Mamá's *tenate*. I'll ask if I may have them."

"Come back tomorrow," the missionary said. "I'll put the chickens in a small box for you. Your Papá may pay then."

The next morning Chabela and Papá returned to the station wagon. Papá paid for Plumita's present and also bought a piece of wire mesh. The missionary told Papá, "The chickens must have a new pen. Plaster the pen walls with mud, make a thatched roof, and cover the window with this wire. Chickens need air, yet they must be kept safe from swooping hawks and prowling coyotes."

To Chabela he gave a paper bag. "This is meat meal mixed with bran. Feed it to your chickens every day, and they will grow into fine big ones."

Later that day, riding home on the hard train seats and up the mountain on the burro's back, Chabela held Mamá's *tenate* with the chirruping chickens inside. Home at last, tired and sleepy, she lifted each one from the box. She slipped them into the nest under Plumita's feathers. "I'm home, Plumita! You'll see your present in the morning."

The next day and on the days that followed, while Papá built her pen, Plumita paraded inside the house and out, followed closely by four small turkeys, six small chickens, and Chabela.

The neighbors came to see Plumita's fine family in their pen. When the chickens were grown and began to lay, the news of them spread up and down and across the mountain. Such large eggs had never before been seen by the mountain people. Almost every day some passers-by stopped to look and exclaim and question. "What big eggs! What fine big chickens! Where did you get them?"

Chabela told each one, "From the missionary. He has enough for you, too. He will tell you how to feed them and take care of them. And he has other good things to tell you, too."

Through Chabela and Plumita's present, the people of the mountainside came to discover the missionaries and the good things that they taught.

—*Elizabeth Allstrom. From " The Singing Secret."*

NEW WORDS IN THE STORY

Abuelita	ah-bway-LEE-tah
adiós	ah-dee-OHS
Buenos días	BWAY-nohs DEE-ahs
Chabela	chah-BAY-lah
limonada	lee-moh-NAH-dah
Mamá	mah-MAH
masa	MAH-sah
Papá	pah-PAH
Pedro	PAY-droh
Plumita	ploo-MEE-tah
tenate	tay-NAH-tay
tortilla	tawr-TEE-yah

Ton Nohon

CHANO took his hoe and hurried along the village street toward his cornfield. All around his small Aztec village of Xalacapan in the tall mountains of Mexico there were corn and beanfields. Chano's field really belonged to his uncle. But, as usual, Uncle had been drinking rum, and rum made him forget his cornfield. Chano was only thirteen and yet he had had to leave his school in the valley and return to the hills to look after his uncle's fields.

The sun was shining hot on the hills and Chano unloosened the ankle bands on his white trousers and rolled his trousers high on his brown legs. He pushed his big hat back from his forehead and put his hoe on his shoulder. Now he was ready for the field.

Chano was turning to go down the hillside trail when suddenly he saw a strange sight. In a circle of Indian men and boys stood a man with white skin and yellow hair. As though the man with yellow hair were not strange enough in himself, he was holding out something for everyone to see. It was a round box, and its glass top glittered in the bright sunshine. The man was not saying a word—just holding the box and waiting. Chano went close enough to see a metal needle quivering inside.

"Ton nohon? What is it?" Chano burst out in Aztec. At

this, the stranger smiled, as though those words were the very thing he had been waiting for someone to say.

"Ton nohon?" Chano asked again.

"Ton nohon?" The stranger repeated the words with such exactness that it was funny. He took a little book from his pocket and wrote something in it. Then, for Chano's sake, he pointed to the sun and the four directions, trying to explain without words what the compass was. But soon he stuffed the little instrument into his pocket and said again, *"Ton nohon?"* as he pointed to the hoe held by Lupito, a friend of Chano's.

"No salon, my hoe," said Lupito.

The man touched Juan's big straw hat, saying, *"Ton nohon?"*

"Yekawiloni," giggled Juan.

It was plain now that the stranger had used the compass to make someone say, "What is it?" in Aztec. Now he could use the question to learn the Aztec names for all manner of things in the village.

"Ton nohon—ton nohon—ton nohon?" the stranger asked again and again. Each time the boys answered in chorus. Each time the stranger said the word after them and wrote it in his book. Next he pointed to himself, saying slowly, "McKinlay—Arch McKinlay."

"Señor McKinlay," the boys said politely. While the Indians in the hills had kept their own Aztec speech, a few Spanish words such as "Señor" were known by all. Also many of the Indians had Spanish names.

The men of the village had stood watching while the stranger questioned the boys. Now Chano saw them moving away. One was muttering, *"Gringo,* foreigner." Another said, "Trader."

"Why does he come to our hills?" they questioned. "Why does he want Aztec words?"

"He spies on our crops, our market. The government will raise the taxes. Already too high. Aztecs are poor." Another grunted his suspicion and moved farther away. Just as well for proud Aztecs not to be spied upon!

Everyone was leaving the white man. For a few minutes, in their curiosity over the little box, the people had forgotten their pride and their suspicion of all strangers. Now they remembered.

Chano, like all the Indian boys of these hills, had heard many stories about the ancient glory of his Aztec people—their beautiful temples, their gold and silver ornaments, their songs and dances. He knew that long ago foreigners had come and robbed them, and ruled over them with little thought for their welfare, until now they were too poor and discouraged to care much even about their cornfields. Chano also was suspicious of strangers.

"*Gracias,* thank you," Señor McKinlay was calling after them, as he smiled and bowed. He could speak Spanish! Unlike most of the other boys, Chano understood his words. He had learned to speak and read Spanish in the school in the valley.

In the field, Chano's hoe scraped and rang, scraped and rang, but for the life of him, he could not make it go deep enough or with its usual rhythm. Wondering seemed to make it wobble and jerk. Trader! Spy! What if the Señor really were a spy? The thought was too exciting for Chano and he had to run over to Lupito's field to talk it over.

"The Señor speaks Spanish. He is a trader or a priest," declared Lupito.

"Why should he want Aztec words?" demanded Chano.

"The priest who comes to the chapel speaks only Spanish. No one understands him, but that is the way one must speak to God—in Spanish. The traders cheat us with their Spanish words," went on Lupito.

"This Señor shall not cheat me. I will talk to him in Spanish," said Chano.

Suddenly Juan came hurrying from the village to tell what he had heard. The Señor had a wife and a little daughter who had blue eyes and yellow hair. He had rented a house in the village. He had come to stay!

"Tomorrow is market day," said Chano. "I will talk to him in Spanish. I will find out why he has come."

"If this *Ton nohon* is a spy," laughed Lupito, "we will drive him from Xalacapan."

With great glee the boys decided to name the stranger *Ton nohon*.

The next day Chano was one of the first to arrive at the weekly market of Xalacapan. Before he had set down his load of last year's corn from his back, he saw the stranger. There he was, still smiling, still asking, *"Ton nohon?"* and writing in his little book. If ever there was a place to learn the names of things Aztec, it was right here in the market—corn, beans, peppers, blankets, shawls, hats, mats, cloth, flowers, babies, baskets, and boys and girls.

The Señor had seen Chano and came toward him. Chano narrowed his eyes to slits out of which he could look his haughty suspicion. You would have thought he was an ancient Aztec chieftain meeting the first Spanish conquerors.

"Why have you come?" Chano asked the Señor in Spanish.

"You speak Spanish!" exclaimed the Señor with joy. "You are the very person who can help me." Then he remembered Chano's question and said, "I have come from the United States to bring a story to your people, and I want Aztec words so that I can give the story to them in their own language."

Chano's eyes grew big. He had heard of the United States and knew that it was far away.

Who, thought Chano, would come all the way from the United States to tell his people a story? Besides, his tribe had many wonderful stories of their own about the days of long ago when the Aztecs had built beautiful temples to their sun god.

"The story is in the Bible," said the Señor, as he took a black book out of his pocket. It looked like the book that the Spanish priest held in his hands when he stood before the images in the chapel. But Chano could not be sure. He had never looked into a Bible. No Aztecs had Bibles.

"Come to my house in Avenida Hidalgo and we shall read the story in Spanish," urged Señor McKinlay.

Chano hesitated, wondering whether he dared to go. He did want to discover why the stranger had come. And he did like stories. He began trying to sell his corn, and when it was gone he followed the Señor to his home.

Just before he entered the house, he hesitated. Would it be safe? Suddenly a little girl with blue eyes, a blue dress, and golden hair ran out to meet the Señor. Now Chano felt that everything was all right. The little girl's mother greeted him with smiles and they all went into the house. The Señor opened the Bible and began to read.

Oh! It was a very exciting story that was read. It was about a young man who left his good home and his kind old father and went off and spent all his money foolishly. When he came home, his father forgave him because he loved him so much.

Chano's eyes were sparkling with interest when Señor McKinlay finished reading. "God loves the Aztecs as the father in the story loved his son," said Señor McKinlay. "He wants them to be great again, to make beautiful things with their hands, to help one another in the fields, to have schools, to sing and dance again as they used to."

Chano's eyes were growing wider and wider. This stranger knew the secrets of his people. He knew that they had once been great. He even knew the things that they would like to do. Truly, the stranger was not a spy, but a friend. Chano wanted to run and tell Juan and Lupito at once.

"We must put the story into Aztec words," said Señor Mc-Kinlay, "so that every home in the tribe may have it—even the homes on the farthest hills. You can speak Spanish. You can help me to change the Spanish words to Aztec. Will you help to give the story to your people?"

Before he ran off to tell Lupito and Juan, Chano said that he would help.

After that, Chano went every day to the Señor's house and sat beside him at the table, where the Bible lay open at the story of the young man who left home. The Señor would read a sentence in Spanish. Chano would think carefully, then say it in Aztec words. They would talk it over and try to find the very best Aztec word for each Spanish one. Señor Mc-Kinlay would write the sentence in his book. Lupito and Juan came sometimes. They watched and listened, and began to read Aztec words, too.

When the story was finished, Señor McKinlay had it printed.

One morning when Chano arrived at the Señor's, the table was covered with piles of yellow booklets. Chano took one in his hand. *"In Ome Te-konewan,* The Two Sons," Chano read the Aztec words on the cover. Then he turned the four pages and with pride read the Bible story of the Prodigal Son he had helped to translate.

Chano took a copy home to his uncle. Uncle was so proud and pleased that he went into the cornfields and hoed, so that Chano could help the Señor turn more Bible stories into Aztec for the tribe.

In time, the Bible stories went into the Aztec homes, even the ones on the farthest hills. And that is how the Aztecs in the mountains of Mexico began to know of God's love for them.

—Gertrude Jenness Rinden. From "Around the World with the Bible."

NEW WORDS IN THE STORY

Avenida Hidalgo	ah-vay-NEE-dah ee-DAHL-goh
Chano	CHAH-noh
gracias	GRAH-see-ahs
gringo	GREENG-goh
In Ome Te-konewan	in oh-meh te-koh-neh-won
Juan	hwahn
Lupito	loo-PEE-toh
no salon	noh sah-LON
Señor	say-NYOR
Ton nohon	ton noh-ON
Xalacapan	shah-lah-KAH-pahn
yekawiloni	yeh-kah-wee-LOH-nee

God's Gift to Paquito

PAQUITO'S village was perched on a hillside on the island of Puerto Rico. In his small house there was always work to do, but most of the time seven-year-old Paquito didn't like to help do it.

Usually when Mamá called, "Go to the store," or "Bring the water," Paquito grumbled. Then sometimes when Mamá didn't ask him at all, the full pail of water would be in the corner, the rice and beans on the table. Paquito liked to help when he thought of it himself.

One morning when Paquito had finished breakfast, he hurried out as usual to find his friends. He did not wash his face as Mamá asked nor put on a clean shirt nor go to the store. He thought only about playing.

On this morning as Paquito and his friends played a game called "The Stick" in a cleared space at the edge of the village, the rumbling sound of a truck came from the distance.

"¿Qué pasa? What goes on here?" Paquito asked. Usually only oxcarts, donkeys, and people on foot traveled over the narrow paths. Few village paths were wide enough for heavy truck wheels.

The sound came nearer, and the boys stopped their game to listen. Was this truck coming to their village? Why?

In another moment, the truck came into view and bumped

its way across the play space to a noisy stop. Two men climbed out of the cab, went to the back, and began to unpack.

Paquito and his friends moved closer. Curious, Paquito spoke out, *"¿Qué pasa?"*

One of the men answered, pointing to the stacks of heavy brown cloth and to the long wooden poles now lying on the ground beside the truck. "I am a pastor, and this is a tent. When it is put up, there will be church meetings in it. Fathers and mothers will come at night. Children are invited for stories and songs. Come when you hear the gong this afternoon."

To Paquito the afternoon seemed a long way off, and he was more interested in the game. "It's my turn," he reminded the boys. "Let's play."

His friends paid no attention. They wanted to watch what the strangers were doing. They told the men, "We'll help you."

The men seemed pleased. "That will be fine," the pastor said. "You're hardly strong enough to pound the heavy stakes into the ground to hold the tent or tall enough to pull the ropes tight and tie the tent firmly in place. But I know a way you can help. You are just the right size to carry benches. You may bring some from your homes for us to use inside the tent."

"¡Sí! ¡Sí! Yes, oh, yes!" the boys answered and hurried to their homes on their errand.

It was no fun to play alone. Paquito went home, too. Mamá was ironing. Paquito sat in the doorway. He sat there a long time, until the gong sounded clang, clang, clang.

"It's the pastor in the tent," Paquito told Mamá. "He came in a truck this morning. I must go to the tent now for stories."

Mamá stopped her ironing. "Paquito *mío,* you go first to the store to buy beans and rice for supper. The shelf is empty."

"But Mamá," Paquito grumbled, "the stories!"

Mamá took coins from a box and handed them to Paquito.

Still grumbling, he took them and ran out through the gate to the store. When he came back, he dropped the bag on the table.

Mamá spoke again. "There is no water, Paquito *mío*. Go now and get it for me."

Mamá pointed to the pail. Paquito took it, dashed through the gate to the village well, and brought back the water as Mamá asked.

"Already I am late," he complained. "The others are in the tent." If only he had offered to help with the benches, he'd be there, too! But Mamá was talking again. "Paquito *mío,* you must have a clean face and a clean shirt when you go to listen to the stories."

Paquito, still complaining, dipped some of the water into a pan, splashed it on his face, then put on the fresh shirt Mamá handed to him.

At last, Mamá was satisfied, and Paquito hurried through the gate.

At the tent the story had begun. Paquito, late, tried to listen, but he could not keep his mind on the pastor's words. His starched shirt was scratchy. He wiggled and wiggled, but the moving around did not make him comfortable. Colorful butterflies darted over his head. One lit on his shoulder, but Paquito could not catch it. Ladybugs came from their hiding places in the grassy tufts and crawled over his bare toes. Paquito reached down, picked up one, and put it into his pocket.

When he straightened up, the pastor was looking at him and speaking directly to him. "God has given a special gift to you. You must use your gift."

The pastor pointed to one then another of the children and repeated, "You, and you, and you also have a special gift from God."

Paquito glanced around. He was sure there was a mistake. A gift from God for him? He had no gift from the good God.

There was not even a gift from Mamá. Money at their house was spent for food, not gifts.

Now the pastor spoke the closing prayer. The meeting was over.

The other children stood up to leave. Paquito also stood up. "Mamá comes tonight," he remembered. "She will ask about this gift, then I will know." But it was a long time to wait until tonight, and suppose Mamá did not come?

Paquito walked slowly up to the pastor. "I have no gift," he said.

The pastor's eyes twinkled as he answered. "I spoke the truth. You have a gift. Perhaps it is because you do not use your gift that you do not know about it. God has given it to you."

His glance was so friendly that Paquito smiled back. He would try to find the gift! All the way home, Paquito thought about it. When did God bring his gift? Where did God leave it?

At home Paquito searched in all the places he knew—on the shelf, behind the door, under the window. He found nothing.

Next morning Paquito told Mamá, "I'll bring the water!" The gift might be near the well. At the well Paquito saw only the usual things.

Back home again he told Mamá, "I'll go for rice and beans." The gift might be hidden along the path to the store. Paquito's eyes searched both sides of the path, but there were only many high weeds and a few small stones.

That afternoon Paquito remembered himself to wash his face and put on a clean shirt. He waited for the gong, and when it sounded, he darted through the gate and turned down the path that led to the tent. He would be on time today! He would find out more about the gift.

But there ahead, and in his way, Paquito saw a small donkey

lying down in the path. Bent over the donkey was his old master, yelling angrily, pulling, tugging at the reins, trying to get the stubborn little creature to his feet.

In his hurry around the donkey and his master, Paquito stopped suddenly. "What a trouble!" he said. Scattered over the ground were vegetables—peppers, squash, beans—spilled out of the baskets on the donkey's back when the creature had decided to rest instead of walking on to the market.

"What a trouble! So much to pick up! No wonder the old man yells." Paquito passed by and went on his way. But not far!

In a moment he was back. "I'll help you," he called to the old man. Without waiting for an answer, Paquito scrambled around, picked up the vegetables, and put them into the baskets.

Suddenly the donkey, with a quick toss of his head and a shake of his body, got up on his feet. The old man was soon astride him and ready to continue his trip. He turned to Paquito.

"*Gracias, gracias,* thank you, thank you. In truth, your two hands are gifts from God himself, and you have used them well to help me this day."

He snapped the reins, and the donkey moved off as though there had been no trouble.

Paquito stared down at his two hands. Were these a gift from God? Could the pastor in the tent have meant hands?

Paquito ran all the way to the tent and straight up to the front where the pastor stood, ready to begin the story. "I've found God's gift! I've had it all the time!"

The next day, and almost every day after that, Paquito remembered to use his gift.

—Elizabeth Allstrom. From "The Singing Secret."

NEW WORDS IN THE STORY

gracias	GRAH-see-ahs
Mamá	mah-MAH
mío	MEE-oh
Paquito	pah-KEE-toh
Qué pasa?	kay PAH-sah
sí	see

Omen and the Jumbies

OMEN was not the only one to shiver at the threat, "The Jumbies will get you." Any child on the lush green Caribbean island of Trinidad would do anything to keep away from Jumbies. Grown people, too, were afraid of them.

It was the slaves who first brought the fear of Jumbies to Trinidad when they came as captives from their homes in Africa, many years ago. Later they taught their Jumby superstitions to the gentle, dark-skinned East Indians who were brought to Trinidad as laborers after the African slaves were freed. So, Negroes and East Indians alike would tremble at the words, "The Jumbies will get you."

Omen was one of the East Indians, a small, shy girl with shiny black hair. She had never seen a Jumby. In fact, she had never known anyone who had actually seen one. But she had heard plenty of stories about them. They were in the air everywhere, the spirits of the dead. Omen and her friends believed that they were lurking in the most unexpected places, ready to do mischief. There might be a few good Jumbies, folks said, but most of them were evil spirits. It was wise, Omen was told, to keep your head covered, or the Jumbies would get in your hair. It was terribly important, Omen knew, to shut your windows and doors tight at night to prevent their sneaking into your house. Any trouble, big or little, Omen heard blamed on the Jumbies. She must never make them angry. Everyone knew that the revenge of a Jumby could be a terrible thing.

Is it any wonder that Omen was frightened to go to the Hummingbird Home, where many girls were cared for by Miss Clark and Miss Winslow, two white women from faraway Canada? The rooms were so big, and the girls were all strangers. She would miss her mother, especially at night when the whole family were used to crowding close together in their tiny house with doors and window shutters closed tight against the Jumbies. Since her father's death, Omen had depended more than ever on the nearness of her mother and her older brothers and sisters.

It was a hard day for Omen when her mother gathered her children about her and said, "I have found work on the roads. I must be away from home many hours each day. You children are big enough to take care of yourselves while I am away— all except Omen. The ladies at the Hummingbird Home will take care of her."

"Must I go?" Omen asked. "I want to stay with you."

"But you cannot stay here because I cannot be at home to take care of you," her mother patiently explained. "Now that your father is dead, I must go out every day to work on the roads. Someone has to earn money for our family."

"But couldn't I stay with neighbors?" Omen begged.

"You would learn nothing from them," her mother answered. "At the Hummingbird Home you will learn many things that are good."

And so Omen, with her tiny bundle of belongings, joined the girls at the Hummingbird Home. Then her mother was free to earn money carrying dirt for the men who mended the roads that ran between sugar cane fields or between forests of low cacao trees sheltered by the high immortelle trees.

At the Home, Omen soon lost her shyness—in the daytime. She would join in the games, such as:

There's a brown girl in a ring,
Tra, la, la, la, la,
There's a brown girl in a ring,
Tra, la, la, la, la,
There's a brown girl in a ring,
Tra, la, la, la, la,
For she's sweet like a sugar and a plum, plum, plum.

She learned how the Home got its name from the old name of the island of Trinidad—*Iere,* which in the old language of the first inhabitants meant Hummingbird. She began to like schoolwork. She learned Bible stories. She liked the verses about God that the girls were learning from the Bible, especially the comforting ones like, "When I am afraid, I put my trust in thee." A small, shy girl separated from her mother needed to know that God was taking care of her.

Omen could not believe Miss Clark and Miss Winslow when they told her that there were no Jumbies, but she did try to think that the God they talked about might be stronger than the Jumbies. He was so much nicer than Jumbies! She would like to think that he was stronger. He loved everyone, even small, shy girls. Jumbies did not love anybody. Omen wished she could believe all that her teachers said.

Omen would sometimes forget about Jumbies all day long. It was at night that she longed for her own tiny house, with all its doors and windows closed tight against the Jumbies, where she could snuggle close to her mother. The white ladies from Canada were so careless about open windows at night. They made a fuss about an open screen but did not seem to care what happened to windows. They thought that mosquitoes were more dangerous than Jumbies.

"Do screens keep out the Jumbies?" Omen used to ask them.

"Please, dear Omen," they would say as they hugged her tight, "do believe us that there are no Jumbies anywhere in the world."

One windy night the girls were all tucked in bed. Prayers had been said. Lights were out—all but the dim light down the hall in a teacher's room. Omen was in bed all by herself—such a lonely way to sleep. There were other girls in the big room, but they were not allowed to talk after lights were out. There was nothing to do but lie there in the dark and wonder about the Jumbies and other things. Omen was not thinking about Jumbies so much as she used to, but still they were in the back of her mind, mixed up with new things like school, Brownies, Bible verses, prayers, games, new friends.

It was quiet in the big room. There were no sounds to be heard as one little girl after another fell asleep. Omen's thoughts grew more and more mixed. In a minute she would be drifting off to sleep also. There was a light step in the hall, pausing at the door, then going away. It was Miss Clark making sure that all was well in the big room of girls. Then it was perfectly still. The last girl had fallen asleep. To the quiet breathing of the girls was added the sound of fluttering window curtains as the wind changed.

Suddenly at the window there was a terrible noise halfway between a scream and a moan. "Squ-e-e-e, scr-e-e-e. Squ-e-e-e, scr-e-e-e." In a moment the girls were wide awake. There were creaks all over the room as one after another sat up in bed.

"Jumbies!" screamed one.

"Jumbies!" The scream came from one bed after another. "Jumbies! Jumbies! Jumbies!"

"Squ-e-e-e, scr-e-e-e," moaned from the window.

Then the beds creaked again as one girl after another dived back under her blanket and tried to hide by pulling it over her head. No girl burrowed deeper within her blanket than Omen. She lay there wondering what she had done that day to anger the Jumbies. It was hard to tell. They could be angry about the strangest things. Omen was remembering stories she had heard about the evil deeds of Jumbies. The more she thought, the stiller she lay, hoping that they would not be able to find her. "Squ-e-e-e, scr-e-e-e." Would it never stop?

Then suddenly Omen remembered what her teachers had said about Jumbies. She remembered what they had said about God who loved everyone, even a small, shy girl.

"It's probably Jumbies I hear," Omen was thinking. "But what does that matter if God is stronger than Jumbies?"

Omen threw back her blanket. She sat up in bed and spoke in a loud clear voice. She sounded so calm that the other girls stopped squealing about Jumbies to listen to her.

"When I am afraid, I put my trust in thee!" said Omen. And then, just to persuade herself that she really meant it, she repeated the Bible verse over again, "When I am afraid, I put my trust in thee!"

There were no more cries of "Jumbies!" The girls were all remembering the story they had heard when they learned that verse from Psalm Fifty-six. They were a little ashamed of their fears—but still the noise kept up at the window. It was a sort of scream, a sort of groan, a sort of moan. One girl after another would risk a peek from under her blanket but duck back when the noise repeated itself, "Squ-e-e-e, scr-e-e-e."

Omen put one foot on the floor. "When I am afraid, I put my trust in thee!" She was truly praying as she said the Bible verse. She put the other foot on the floor. Blankets all over the room were thrown back, just a crack, as dark eyes watched to see what she would do.

She walked slowly across the room toward the window, straight toward that Jumby-like sound. She opened the window wide and stood beside it. Blankets were thrown back farther, as girls stared to see what would happen to Omen, who dared defy the Jumbies. For a minute nothing happened, nothing but the screeching moan, "Squ-e-e-e, scr-e-e-e."

Omen stood at the window—looking—listening—thinking. Suddenly she laughed. At first it was a nervous little laugh.

Then it grew into a big amused laugh. It was such a laugh that the girls found themselves hearing it instead of the squ-e-e-e, scr-e-e-e that moaned behind it. It was such a laugh that teachers' doors all up and down the corridor were flung open and footsteps hurried to the girls' room.

"What is it, Omen?" Girls were sitting up in bed now.

"Isn't it a Jumby?" Girls ventured timid feet to the floor.

"Why do you laugh, Omen?" Girls were taking careful steps toward the window with its steady squ-e-e-e, scr-e-e-e.

"Come and see," giggled Omen.

The bravest girls reached the window and looked out. In about half a minute they were laughing with Omen.

"Girls! Girls!" It was Miss Winslow in the doorway. "What is the meaning of this? You are out of bed. You're laughing. What has happened?"

"Listen!" said one of the girls.

"Squ-e-e-e, scr-e-e-e," was what the teachers heard.

"We thought it was Jumbies," said another of the girls. "Omen was the only one who dared look."

"And what did you find, Omen?" asked Miss Clark.

"Just two branches rubbing together," giggled Omen.

There was a very special hug for Omen when she was tucked in bed for the second time that night. And as she snuggled down to sleep, Omen wondered if the teachers might be right after all. Perhaps all Jumbies were nothing worse than branches rubbing together. Omen fell asleep with the squ-e-e-e, scr-e-e-e at the window making a song of the words, "When I am afraid, I put my trust in thee."

> —*Alice Geer Kelsey. From "Many Hands in Many Lands."*

NEW WORDS IN THE STORY

Iere	ee-EH-ray
Omen	OH-men

One World for Johnny

JOHNNY CHEN lived in two worlds. One was a Chinese world. The other was American. Johnny went back and forth between his two worlds every day. He didn't have a space ship to travel in, not even an ordinary ship. There wasn't any wide ocean between Johnny's two worlds—just a few blocks of dingy street in the large city of Los Angeles.

Johnny's Chinese world was his home upstairs over the restaurant where his father and uncles worked. Johnny liked his Chinese home. His mother was always there, making new dresses for his small sisters or cooking good Chinese food for her family. His mother wore a Chinese dress. One black dress she wore had tiny carved gold balls for buttons. These had come from her village in China, where long ago, people had put money into ornaments instead of bank accounts. Johnny thought he would like to tell his friend Carl about those buttons. Carl was a boy who lived in Johnny's other world—his American one. Carl was captain of the baseball team.

There were other things from China in Johnny's home. There was the orange silk lamp shade from Canton that made the light so pretty. There was the polished black table where his mother set the bowls of food and chopsticks. There was a scroll on the wall with a black dragon on it. The dragon writhed and twisted up and down the long, narrow scroll. If

Carl ever saw that dragon, he would ask a hundred questions. But Carl would never see it because he lived in that other world.

In Johnny's home the talking was all Chinese. His mother couldn't speak any English at all. Even the cat spoke Chinese. When she was hungry, she said, *"Yao, yao."* That meant, "Want, want." When she was happy, she purred, *"Hao, hao."* That meant, "Good, good." If Johnny spoke to her in English, she looked disdainful and walked away.

Johnny liked his Chinese world when he was in it, but he wished that somehow his two worlds would come together. He didn't like to live in two separate worlds.

Johnny's American world was at All People's. The whole name for it was All People's Christian Church and Community Center. Well, of course he went to school, where he was in the fifth grade and very bright, too, but the place where he played and went to club meetings and was on a team was at All People's. At All People's, Johnny felt like a real American. Everybody did. The minister never said, "The Chinese" nor "The Japanese" nor "The Mexicans." He said, "Johnny" or "Mrs. Tomo" or "Mr. Valentes." He called each person by his name and not by the country where his ancestors had come from. When Johnny sat in church at All People's on Sunday morning and looked around him, he wished that his mother could come here, too. He knew that she would like it. When he peeked into the club rooms and saw the women sewing, laughing, and chatting, he wished that his mother would join a club. But she was afraid to come. She was afraid of everything in America. Because she couldn't speak English, she was afraid to leave her own neighborhood. That was what kept Johnny's two worlds apart.

One morning after church, when Johnny was going out of All People's, he saw Mrs. Lin standing in her doorway across the street. She was waving a letter.

"It's Auntie Lin," Johnny said to his friend Carl. Mrs. Lin was not a relative, but Johnny used the Chinese way of calling a good friend Auntie.

"The letter is from her son in Korea. Good-by. She wants me to read it to her."

"Wait a minute," Carl said, as he grabbed Johnny by the shoulder. "You say she's got a son in the army in Korea, and she can't read his letter? How come?"

"Her son was born here in America and writes only English. She can't read English."

"She lives right here all this time and can't read English?"

Johnny stiffened a little. "She came to America when she was a big woman. There was no school for her."

"How do you like that! A woman and can't read her own son's letter."

Johnny was very glad now that he had never invited Carl to his home.

"Can I go with you while you read the letter to her?" Carl asked now.

"It's better I read it to Auntie Lin alone," Johnny said coldly.

Then Johnny thought it over. James Lin's letters were always interesting. It would be good for Carl to hear a fine letter written by a Chinese American who was in the army of the United Nations. "Then come," he said.

While Johnny was bowing to Mrs. Lin, Carl looked at her. He wanted to see what a woman who couldn't read and who could speak only a little English looked like. Mrs. Lin had a wide, smiling face. She was half saying hello and half sighing her shame because she couldn't read.

"Auntie Lin," Johnny said, "may I read your letter to you?" He said it very slowly so that Auntie Lin would not be ashamed before Carl.

"Please, please, young scholar," Auntie Lin said brokenly. "I am dumb. I am foolish. Cannot read. I trouble you."

"No, no, Auntie, it isn't any trouble at all."

"My gosh, why doesn't he take the letter and read it?" Carl said to himself. "Why is he so polite?"

Johnny introduced Carl, and they went inside. Carl grinned when Auntie Lin brought in some sponge cakes. Carl ate one after another before he noticed that Johnny hadn't touched one. Johnny read the letter out loud in English twice to know its meaning before he translated it into Chinese. It was an exciting letter. Mrs. Lin had sent her son James some clothes for Korean children. He had given them to a boy and girl near his camp. He had given them chocolate bars, too, from the army store. And he had played with them. Then James had to move camp. His army truck was all packed. He looked around to say good-by to his little Korean friends. They weren't anywhere around. "Must be hiding," James Lin had thought, and he decided it would be too sad to say good-by to them anyway, so he had started off. He had gone six miles when the men in the truck called to him to stop. They had found his little Korean friends hiding in the truck under some blankets. James had to turn around and take the children back home. They had wanted to go with him to the next camp.

Carl was glad to hear the letter twice. But now Johnny was putting all the words into Chinese, and Auntie Lin was laughing and crying.

"Again one more time?" Johnny was offering. Carl was glad to hear it even a fourth time. Though he couldn't understand a single Chinese word, he was understanding his friend Johnny better than ever before. Before, he had thought of Johnny as extra smart in school and extra quick in games. Now he was seeing Johnny in a new way. Johnny was so gentle and kind to Mrs. Lin that Carl felt awkward and foolish beside him. Carl decided that Johnny had something special about him because he was Chinese. Carl had a feeling that his mother would like Johnny very much.

Johnny would not take the envelope of money that Mrs. Lin was urging on him. "Not necessary," he said. "Moreover, I will come after club tomorrow and read it one more time."

"You read better than Mr. Fu in the grocery," Auntie Lin said as she tried to pay Johnny. "He reads it only once and too fast."

"Gee! What would it be like to have to pay to have letters read to you?" Carl was thinking. And when they were out on the street, he said this to Johnny.

"It is not really living in America," Johnny said. "And if you cannot understand English, you are always a little afraid."

"Gosh!" Carl said. And because he didn't know what else to say, he stopped and kicked a hydrant. Johnny could feel Carl's friendship and he said, "My mother doesn't speak any English."

"Your mother?" Carl showed his surprise. "But you're just like an American."

"I am American. I was born here."

"Gosh!" Carl said and kicked the hydrant some more.

"If I didn't have All People's, I would be like my mother. Afraid of America."

"I guess you like All People's."

"Of course," Johnny grinned. "There I feel I am American."

"Sure, when you wear your T shirt with A.P.C.C. across the front and play baseball—well—we're all the same."

"And another time, too," Johnny said.

"When?"

"At the bread and water banquet," Johnny said. He meant the time each year when the church saved the cost of a meal and sent the money to missions.

"You're crazy, Johnny. I hate bread and water."

"I hate, too," Johnny grinned. "Cold bread! Cold water! Terrible."

"Then why did you say you liked it?"

"I did not say I liked the food. I said I liked the feeling at that time. If I eat such a meal with the church, to send money away, I am really an American."

"Gee, Johnny, you're queer."

Johnny thought he had better not try any more to tell his deep down feelings to another boy, even his best friend Carl.

Carl was looking across the street at All People's. "I bet All People's would teach your mother to read," he said. "And Auntie Lin."

"All People's?"

"Sure. They have all kinds of classes. You know that. My mother teaches how to take care of babies."

"My mother is so afraid that I—"

Carl was dashing across the street. "C'mon quick, before the minister leaves. We'll ask him." Johnny, who was always surprised at Carl's abrupt ways, followed. They found the minister locking his study. Soon they were sitting in that study.

"Mrs. Lin's had a letter from her son in Korea and can't read it, and Johnny's mother can't read a word of English, and we wondered if All People's could have an English class for Chinese people." Carl said it all in one breath.

"If there are several who want an English class, of course we will have one," the minister said.

"How many?" Johnny asked.

"Say, six."

"Then, I will discover if six wish it. Thank you so much." The boys said good-by and left.

"Shall I go with you to find the people for the class?" Carl asked Johnny when they were in the street again and walking along together.

Johnny looked worried. He did not want to say no, yet he knew that this big important matter must be handled in the Chinese way. "Such a matter requires Chinese custom," he said.

"What custom?"

"I must go to the elder in our neighborhood. If he says it is all right, my mother will go. So will Auntie Lin."

"Gee, I want to see the elder, too. I like Auntie Lin. And the whole thing was my idea. You tell me what to do, and I'll do what you say."

Johnny laughed. "The elder will serve tea and cakes as soon as we enter. Must not eat at once. Not polite."

"Just look at them? Not touch them?"

"Yes, that is more polite. But later when it is almost time to leave, eat one or two. Not every one!" Johnny laughed some more.

"Gosh! Well, I'll try to remember."

"If the elder likes us, he will order a special hot dish brought in, like old Chinese custom. Can you eat with chopsticks?"

"No! Of course not. Can't you teach me before we go?"

"Come here to All People's at three o'clock. I will bring chopsticks and teach you. Then we can go."

At three o'clock the two boys met. They went downstairs to a club room. "These are for you—a present," Johnny said, handing Carl two red chopsticks that were like long, slender pencils. Then he sprinkled some peanuts onto the table, took up his own chopsticks, and, moving his fingers to work the chopsticks like pincers, picked up a peanut between the two points and put it into his mouth.

"Gee! You hold both chopsticks in one hand? I never knew that." Carl tried. One of his sticks clattered to the floor. He tried again. It looked easy when Johnny did it. Carl's fingers felt stiff. He looked more carefully to see just how Johnny did it.

"Auntie Lin should see you trying so hard," Johnny said. "Such hard work so that she can have an English class."

All of a sudden Carl got the idea. He opened and shut the points like pincers. He picked up a peanut. He held his mouth open very wide. When he got the chopsticks up to his mouth, they were empty. The peanut had dropped out. He was jabbing empty chopsticks into his mouth.

Johnny doubled up with high giggles.

Carl tried again. This time he lifted the peanut all the way to his mouth. "Another, another!" he shouted. "It's fun! I'm always going to eat with chopsticks."

When Johnny thought that Carl had practiced enough, they set out for the elder's home. It was behind the restaurant. As soon as they got there, a slender little woman put tea and cakes on the table between Carl and Johnny. Carl folded his arms stoutly so he wouldn't touch them.

Soon the elder came in. Carl liked his kind, twinkling eyes. He was full of fun and joking. He asked the boys what games they liked best. For a while Johnny didn't speak unless the elder spoke first. After what seemed like a long time to Carl, Johnny explained about the English class at the church. The elder seemed very pleased. He named several men who would like to study English. Johnny got up his courage to suggest Auntie Lin and his own mother and another woman. The elder nodded.

When the business was settled, the elder ordered bowls of noodles brought in—a big flared bowl for each boy. The noodles were fresh and hot and yellow, with chicken and almonds on top.

Johnny picked up his chopsticks, pinched some noodles into them, and lifted the long strands to his mouth.

Carl tried to do the same. His strands slipped right back into the bowl. "Noodles are harder than peanuts," he said. "I can't do it."

"Try hard," Johnny whispered. "The elder will be pleased to see you eat with chopsticks."

Carl made a desperate effort. He had to please the elder. Several tries, and just as before, he suddenly had the knack of it. "Mmmm-hmmmm. Boy! That's good!" he said. "Wish my mother could make this."

"You can have this at my house if you will come," Johnny said.

"You bet I'll come!" Carl said. "And we'll speak English, and your mother will hear us, and she will learn fast."

Johnny smiled. At last his two worlds were beginning to come together into one.

> —*Gertrude Jenness Rinden. From "Sidewalk Kids."*

NEW WORDS IN THE STORY

Chen	chehn
Fu	foo
hao	hah-oh
Lin	lin
yao	yah-oh

Aunt Sue's Bible Day

SALLY was a little Negro girl who lived with her Aunt Sue in a cabin in the clearing, way back from the bus road in the state of North Carolina. The neighbors said that Sally was about the prettiest child they had ever seen.

"It's because Aunt Sue loves her so. That makes her look so happy and so pretty," they said. "You just couldn't help being happy, living with Aunt Sue."

Day after day went along about the same in the cabin in the clearing—washing, baking, helping the neighbors. But every so often came that special day that was different. In many ways Sally could feel that day coming, but the surest sign was when Aunt Sue went to the cupboard and took out her big flowered dress, and chucked it into a tub of foaming suds. As Sally watched the wind whipping the dress back and forth, back and forth on the line, she knew the day was coming. Tomorrow would be Bible day!

Sure enough, the next morning the bed would creak extra early, and Aunt Sue would be up and hurrying around. Sally would jump up, too, for in no time Aunt Sue would be off down the road to take the bus to other clearings and towns, where she would go from door to door to sell her Bibles. Sally was as proud as could be of what Auntie did. When she was just a little tot, Sally had learned to say with great importance,

"Auntie is a volunteer worker for the American Bible Society. She wants every Negro family in our state to have a Bible."

As soon as the breakfast dishes were cleared away, and the checkered tablecloth shaken and smoothed again, Aunt Sue would go to the cupboard and begin to hand down the Bibles and Testaments and Gospels. Sally would stack them neatly— all the light blue Matthews, the red Lukes, the pink Johns, the purple Marks—in separate piles to be tied together. Into Aunt Sue's big brown bag would go the whole Bibles first of all, then the New Testaments, and then the Gospels.

But right here Sally's share in the adventure always ended. Aunt Sue, who loved her so much, had never taken her on the Bible trip.

When the big bag was packed and bulging, Aunt Sue was sure to say, "Here, child, run along to Aunt Miriam's with this loaf of bread. Her poor old hands are so crippled that she can't make bread any more." Or sometimes she would say, "You better run along over to Mrs. Brown's today and help her with the children. She's got so many."

Then Auntie would set off down the long dusty road to the bus. Sometimes she would be gone one day and sometimes two or three days. Sally would stay with the neighbors until she returned.

In the past Sally had been content to hear the wonderful stories that Aunt Sue would bring back from the trip—how she had knocked at door after door, and how so many kinds of faces had come to the doors, "smiling faces and worried faces and tired faces and sweet little faces with big eyes peeking around big skirts." To all those who opened their doors to her Aunt Sue told how the Bible would help them. If there was sickness or trouble, Auntie went right in and lent a hand.

Sometimes Sally gathered the children of the clearing together to act out Bible day. That was fun.

But now that she was nine, Sally was no longer content with

stories or acting out. She wanted to go on the real adventure. For that she had been scheming and planning, and now the day had come.

The big brown bag of books was packed and ready. Auntie began to say, "Sally child, I promised Aunt Miriam some of my fresh bread. Her poor hands are so crippled she can't make any. You better run along." These were the words that Sally had heard so many times.

"All right, I will run along," she thought. "But I'm coming back. I'm going to follow Auntie to the bus. I'm going with her today."

Sally raced to Aunt Miriam's house with the bread. "Here, Aunt Miriam. Here's just a little bread. I'll come back another day to help you." Then she flew out the door.

"Land-a-mercy, what's happened? Anything wrong?" By the time Aunt Miriam shuffled to the door, Sally was flying down the path between the trees.

As she neared her own cabin, Sally slowed down to think about her plans. Suddenly, flutter, flutter, in front of her ran three of Auntie's best laying hens. Laying hens must be caught at once, before they were lost in the woods. With the first two, Sally was lucky. Back into the pen she stuffed them. But the third one ran under the cabin. There was nothing to do but scramble after it. Squawk! Squawk! She—no—yes—she had it. And now she began to scramble out. What was that? Auntie was talking to one of the neighbors in the kitchen.

"I want to take her with me, but it's a long, hard trip. Sometimes the bus doesn't stop for me. Sometimes I have to stand up. It would just break my heart if the bus was crowded and she heard them say, 'No room for niggers.'"

Sally was listening so hard that she forgot the hen. Squawk! It was getting away. She grabbed it and stuffed its head under her apron. All the time she was thinking hard.

So the Bible day trip that she had always supposed was a

great adventure wasn't so easy, after all. And that was why Auntie hadn't ever taken her. "But if it's like that, she needs me to help her," thought Sally. "I've got to go with her now."

Quickly Sally took off her apron and wrapped it around the hen to muffle the squawks. Then she tiptoed to the pen and set the wriggling apron inside. The hen fluttered free. Sally tiptoed across the path to the side door of the house, crept across the sitting room, and took her green hat and coat and red pocketbook from the hook. Creak! Creak! Every board seemed to shout. At last she was outside and running toward the bus stop. The road was hot and dusty and Sally soon stopped running. She thought of Auntie and her heavy bag. She wanted to go back and help her, but she couldn't take any chances on being sent home. So she went on until she came to the wide black road along which the bus would come.

"I'm going with you, I've decided," shouted Sally, as Auntie, puffing and panting, came into sight. "You need someone to help you sell all those Bibles."

By the time she got her breath, Aunt Sue knew it was no use to protest. "Land sakes, here comes the bus!" she said. She clutched Sally's hand as the giant, orange bus came swaying down the road. It was slowing down. Good! There had been times when it hadn't even stopped for her. An old man was getting off. Aunt Sue pushed Sally toward the step, but before she could reach it, the driver shouted, "Full up today—no more room for niggers," and thud, the doors shut tight, and the bus, now a hateful monster, hurried down the road.

"There'll be another one along in an hour," said the old man, as he shouldered a bag and started up the road.

"But we can't wait—we wanted to sell Bibles to a lot of people," Sally started to protest. Then she noticed Aunt Sue's eyes. Suddenly she remembered why she had come. "Sit down here on the grass, Auntie, and—and would you like for me to tell you a story?"

Aunt Sue couldn't help chuckling at this. "No, Sally. I'll just take out my Bible and read a little." So she wiped her eyes, and fumbled in her bag, and took out her Bible and began to read. Sally sat on the grass beside her.

"Auntie," asked Sally, after a while, "do white folks read the same Bible as black folks?"

" 'Course they do, Sally child. And the Lord loves white folks and black folks just the same. No matter what happens, all your life you can just remember that." There was a pause, then Aunt Sue went on, "When everyone lives by the Bible, then white folks will love black folks, and black folks will love white folks."

"Listen here, child," said Aunt Sue, and she read from the Bible. " 'And this commandment have we from him, that he who loveth God love his brother also.' " Aunt Sue turned the pages and read other verses. Before they knew it, an hour had gone by.

"Here it comes! Here it comes!" Sally whispered. The big bus was roaring toward them. Sally wanted to shout, but she only dared to whisper because it might not stop. But it was stopping, and—now they were on.

"Full up today. No seats left," the driver said in a kindly way, as Aunt Sue paid two fares.

"Stand close to me," whispered Auntie, and she looked straight ahead out the window.

Sally did not look straight ahead and out the window. I should say not! The whole bus was full of people, and they all had such pretty clothes to look at. There was a woman with a hat all flowers—soft green and yellow. "I could make one just like it with the flowers from the forsythia at home, for when we play Bible day," thought Sally.

There was a man wearing yellow gloves and holding a cane. As Sally looked from person to person, smiles began to come on the faces of each one.

"Pretty, isn't she?" murmured the flower-hat woman to her neighbor.

"Don't you want to sit down, little girl?" she asked as she moved over to make room.

"Oh, no, thank you," said Sally. "But Auntie does, because she's got all those Bibles."

"Got what?" asked the gentleman with the cane.

"Bibles. Her big bag is full of Matthew, Mark, Luke, and John. Auntie wants every Ne—every person in North Carolina to have a Bible."

"Hush, child," Aunt Sue was saying, but it was no use.

Everyone was smiling now except the man who had asked what Auntie had in her bag. He looked very much embarrassed. Sally felt sorry for him. Maybe he didn't know about the Bible.

"The Bible is God's word," she explained. "If white folks live by it, they will love black folks. If black folks live by it, they will love white folks."

"Hush, child," said Auntie, as she pulled at her hand.

"That's what you said, Auntie, when we were sitting on the grass."

"And it's true," said a handsome gentleman as he stood up and reached deeply into his pocket. "I'd like to buy one of your Bibles."

"So would I." . . . "I want one, please." There was a chorus of voices all around the bus. Women opened pretty purses. Men opened leather wallets. Sally, all smiles, gave out Bibles as fast as Auntie took them from the depths of her bag.

"Will we have enough left for all the houses where we are going to knock?" whispered Sally.

"Yes, yes, I brought extras today. And I can see right now it's going to be the best Bible day I've ever had," answered Aunt Sue, smiling.

—Gertrude Jenness Rinden. From "Around the World with the Bible."

The Old Story in a New Land

FATHER ANTOINE shivered slightly, even in the shelter of the log hut. He was cold with the bitter chill of the Canadian northland. But he was colder with loneliness and longing for home. Home, to Father Antoine, was the ordered peace of his monastery, back on the sunny slopes of the southern French hills. Home was the sweet ringing of the chapel bell, the solemn songs of the deep-voiced choir, the conversation about high and holy things.

Father Antoine raised homesick eyes to his surroundings. Outside were the huge pine trees, hung with gleaming snow; the dead stillness of the forest; the snowshoes piled beside the low door of the nearby hunter's lodge. Around and about moved the tall forms of Indians, members of an unfriendly tribe camped nearby for a few days. Their presence made Father Antoine feel that he was indeed a stranger in a foreign land. For it was Christmas Eve! Christmas Eve, and not a soul but faithful Pierre the fur trapper, his guide and companion, to join with him in the Christmas service tomorrow.

Yes, it was Christmas Eve, and all about him were the people of this unfriendly tribe. He had not expected to find them here, near the lonely hut of Pierre, where he had come to rest for a few days. Yet for the sake of just such people he had left the peace and order of the monastery and braved danger and hardship in an unfriendly, new world. Now was his chance to help them.

As the thought took hold of his mind, Father Antoine's heart began to glow once more. Christmas Eve, and here were those who had never heard the most glorious story of all the world. Christmas Eve, and here was he, knowing their language and able, though haltingly, to tell them of that story. The loneliness and cold vanished from the heart of Father Antoine. The wintry woods at which he had shivered not so many minutes ago seemed to sparkle with light and joy.

Father Antoine went hurrying into the woods, filled with the delight of a new idea. He would cut boughs of pine and hemlock and the graceful balsam. He would deck the cabin door and window. Pierre would bring logs and build a mighty fire before the door. They would invite the Indians to come and listen to the Christmas story. As he worked busily to get the greens, Father Antoine began to repeat to himself the story of the angels and the shepherds and the Wise Men. In what words should he tell the story to these Indians?

Father Antoine came to a sudden pause as he worked. He remembered that he did not know the Indian word for sheep; nor for shepherd; nor for camels, as far as that went. "I must ask Pierre," he thought. Then he laughed aloud in the still forest. There would be no such words in the language of the people of the far north woods. They had never seen any sheep. Nor any shepherds! And most certainly no camels!

Father Antoine went slowly on with his work. His mind was busy planning the story in a way which could be understood by the Indians. "Perhaps it is not needful for these forest folk to hear of the beasts that live in Palestine," he said to himself. "I think not. For it is about the wonder and beauty of that first Christmas night that I want to tell them."

Pierre was delighted when he heard Father Antoine's plan. He carried the invitation to the Indian camp. He helped to deck the lodge with pine and spruce and balsam and dark hemlock. He heaped high a pile of logs near the door. Then, when the hour had come, he carried embers from the fire within, and lit the Christmas logs.

It was a strange sight that firelight showed—the keen, bronzed faces, the lean and hardy forms of chiefs and braves, the slender figures and the deep dark eyes of squaws and maidens. Among them were the children, eager to know the news this pale-faced man might bring.

Father Antoine stood upon the threshold of the lodge. He raised his hand. Then in words that sometimes faltered, but with voice strong and clear, he told the Christmas story. And in these words he spoke it.

"It was a night like this," said Father Antoine. "The woods were dark and full of snow. The moon shone bright upon the hills and valleys. Through the woods, traveling to join a gathering of their tribes, there came a man and woman, worn with cold, weary of the trail.

"Night had fallen before they reached the camp. The place was already full. There was no room for them within the wigwams of their friends. No room in any lodge! But she, the squaw, had bitter need of shelter. So at length a place was found, beneath the spreading branches of a mighty pine. There had been heaped the poles on which the wigwam coverings were dragged in travel. There, a sort of shelter was devised where she might rest."

The Indian folk leaned forward to hear better. They knew well how weary one could be from winter travel.

Father Antoine went on. " 'Twas on that very night, within that shelter, that her child was born. There was no bed in which to lay the babe. They placed him on a deerskin, soft as moss, laid in a cradle of soft evergreen. Her brave kept a fire blazing in the open place between the trees. He dared not have the flaming logs beneath the pine tree. But he carried hot coals so as to bring their warmth to the mother and to the child."

Father Antoine paused. This next part of the story was not easy to make clear to those who listened.

"Out on the forest trails," he said, "the hunters of the tribe followed the deer in search of food for their people. When the hunt was over and they had started home, their feet came to a sudden stop upon the trail. They listened. From somewhere there came sounds such as never in their lives had they heard before. It was the music of sweet voices singing. Sweeter than the voice of wind among the treetops; fairer than the sound of rain upon parched forest; softer than the sound of waves lapping upon the lake shore, came the music. Suddenly, before them on the trail, in garments whiter than the snow itself, with great white wings that reached as high as the tallest pine tree, stood a messenger with arms outstretched. The hunters feared not man nor beast, but now they were filled with fearsome wonder. As they stood in awe, the messenger spoke and said, 'In a forest shelter near, a child is just now born. That child is sent by the Great Spirit, for your people's good. Beneath a pine tree, cradled in a deerskin, you will find him.'

"His message given, with quivering wings the messenger floated out of sight. Suddenly all the sky was filled with brightness. Praise to the Great Spirit filled the air."

Father Antoine's very voice was full of wonder as he pictured the scene. He went on with the story. "When the song was finished, and the forest once again lay silent, the hunters hurried to their camp. Beneath the ancient tree they found the child, as the messenger had said, all wrapped in deerskin. Such a tiny babe! So deep and cold the snow! The youngest hunter stripped away the wolfskin he was wearing and wrapped it around the child."

Listening carefully to the story, the squaws nodded their heads. They knew how warm a wolfskin was. The baby in the story would lie snug that night, they knew.

Father Antoine continued. "In those days, three chiefs appeared, striding along the forest trails as if in search of something. They were unarmed and carried gifts. The hunters of the tribe met them along the trails and took them before their leader. All the braves of the tribe gathered to hear what strange errand brought them here.

"The strangers had a curious tale to tell. 'Listen to how the voice of the Great Spirit came to us, in our distant hunting fields,' they said. 'It spoke to us from a glorious star whose light outshone the moon. It told us to seek a child new-born, who later would be the mightiest chief the world will ever know!'

"There were many little Indian babies in the winter camp. How could the strangers know which one was the child they had come to see? They waited for their star. When darkness fell, the waning moon had not yet risen to give light. But a great star's brightness shone in the sky. It seemed to move, then came to quiet rest above the topmost branches of the tree beneath which lay the newborn child.

"Softly through the snow the strangers strode. They came beneath the sheltering branches of the ancient tree. They looked and saw the child. One by one, in silence, each brought out his gift and laid it before the cradleboard on which the child was bound. Rich pelts of beaver were the gift of one. The second brought long strings of wampum. But the third laid by the cradleboard an eagle feather.

"So," said Father Antoine, "was full welcome given to the Son of the Great Spirit who should save his people and the people of the world. When that child became a man, he taught his people of the Great Spirit and how to live in his ways. These ways I have come to teach to you that you also may know."

Father Antoine paused as he finished his story. Then he lifted high his arms above the listening folk. "Great Spirit, Father, God," he prayed, "be here, within this forest and among these folk. Enter their hearts that they may then come to know thy love which sent thy Son to us to teach us of thee."

When the Indians had gone, old Pierre smiled. "Father, I had forgotten it could be Christmas in such a wilderness. But as you talked I felt the same springing joy I used to know at home."

"Christmas is in the heart, Pierre," said Father Antoine. "And I pray that the good God may some day have the love of these wild children of the forest. May their hearts some day be full of Christmas love, and love of God."

The embers of the fire cooled and blackened. Within the close-barred lodge, Father Antoine and old Pierre wrapped themselves in their skins of wolf and otter and lay down to sleep. Their loneliness was gone. They were happy in the memory of the Christmas story spread.

> —*Grace W. McGavran. From "We Gather Together."*

NEW WORDS IN THE STORY

Antoine	an-TWAHN
Pierre	pee-AIR

The School in the Hollow

JIMMY HIGNITE'S long legs swung him down the mountain trail. Jimmy was twelve, but you would have said he was fourteen. Like all his folks in the West Virginia mountains, he had grown up tall and slender.

This particular morning Jimmy's face was washed back behind his ears. The tattered trousers that flopped around his thin legs were clean. He had scrubbed them himself. That was how much Jimmy had liked his first three days at Vacation Bible School in the hollow. If he hadn't liked it, wild mules couldn't have made him wash up and comb up for it. As it was, Granny Hignite had said he had used too much of the precious water that had to be carried all the way from the spring.

"You're wasting water, Jimmy," she had said.

"Miss Kelsey said to wash."

"What does washing have to do with learning the Bible?" Granny in her high-pitched voice had asked. "She told me it was a Bible school. She promised me if I'd let you go, you'd learn the Bible and learn it good."

As for Jimmy, that was the part about the school that surprised him most. It was a Bible school and yet it was fun. All his life Jimmy had heard the Bible preached. His mountain people were religious. Each Sunday, Preacher Wimmer read the Bible in a loud voice, then thundered even louder about the dreadful things that would happen to you if you didn't repent of your sins. Preacher Wimmer's preaching had made Jimmy tiptoe in a wide circle around the big Bible in Granny's cabin. But as for opening it—never! If the flames of hell-fire, such as you saw all the time Preacher Wimmer was preaching, had been leaping up around it, Jimmy could not have avoided it more carefully.

Down there in the rough pine shack where Miss Kelsey had invited the children to vacation school, the Bible was always open in a friendly way. In it Miss Kelsey could find things that didn't frighten you at all. At first Jimmy had thought that Miss Kelsey wasn't reading the Bible right. She didn't raise her voice at all. And she read about Jesus.

Jesus had been a carpenter when he was a boy. He had made benches and yokes and stools. Each boy in the school was to make a bench. Miss Kelsey had asked old Mose to come down from his cabin and teach the boys how to saw and plane and join the boards together to make benches. Jimmy had never had a chance to make anything before. He thought it all over as he hurried down the trail. He wasn't going to miss a day of school.

When Jesus was on earth, he had helped people, who as far as you could tell were a good deal like Granny and Mose. Best of all, Jesus had told stories. The stories were right there in the Bible. Miss Kelsey could find them. They were as good as any of the mountain stories. Take yesterday's. In it Jesus had told about a man who had gone down a lonesome trail and had been robbed and wounded. Two people had passed by and they hadn't helped him. You could just see how it had been. Then a stranger from another place had come along and helped him. Jesus had said that the stranger had been a good neighbor and that neighbors should help one another in such ways.

Jimmy was nearly down the trail. He hurried along so he wouldn't be late. Now he was passing Zeke Carey's cabin. Where was everyone? Only the smallest young ones were in the yard. Oh—the others were down at the school of course! Miss Kelsey had invited even the no'count Carey children to the Bible school. Though there was poverty all through the hills, the Careys were known far and wide for being the poorest and the most shiftless. Not only that, they were the least liked, for Zeke, with his careless shooting, had made many enemies.

Jimmy was hurrying past the cabin. But someone had seen him go by the door and shouted loudly, "Jimmy Hignite, come quick!" It was Mrs. Carey. She came out of the cabin and called, "My baby's scalded herself! She pulled a kettle of water over onto herself when my back was turned. Run quick for the doctor at the mining camp! Run for me, Jimmy Hignite!" Mrs. Carey hurried back into the cabin.

Jimmy stopped and stood still. Getting the doctor would mean going back a piece and then down another trail more than a mile long to the mining camp. It might mean giving up school altogether for that day. Yet the baby must be terribly burned if Mrs. Carey wanted the camp doctor. The mining people in general were considered outsiders and the camp an enemy in the West Virginia hills. The mine took the strength and sometimes the lives of men.

Jimmy thought again. If it were Granny who had asked him, or anyone like that, of course he would go for the doctor. But to go for the Careys was different. Zeke Carey had shot more people in these hills than the average.

A baby's feeble wail came from the cabin. Must be badly burned or it would be crying louder. If it weren't for making that bench, and a perfect attendance, and hearing the story, of course he would go for the doctor.

Jimmy kicked his foot against a tree trunk as he tried to

decide what to do. He turned his back on the house, hoping he could forget the baby. Step by step he shuffled slowly down the trail. "I'm already late for the Bible story," he thought. "And it might be another good one like yesterday's about a neighbor."

Suddenly Jimmy wheeled around. The thought of the story about the good neighbor had made him know what he should do. Bending over, he began to run back up the trail with long strides. He flew past the Carey cabin so fast that he saw only the frightened look on the face of the mother, who stood in the doorway. Up and up he went, racing faster and faster to make up for those shameful minutes he had wasted. He had never known the trail to seem so steep.

At last he came to the fork in the path and started toward the mining camp. Down, down he raced, jolting so fast that, mountain boy though he was, twice he stumbled on the roots and went rolling headlong, then pulled himself up and went on until he reached the mining camp.

Meanwhile, down in the hollow where the vacation school was meeting, the morning had passed pleasantly. The worship service was now coming to a close. The children were singing "Tell Me the Stories of Jesus." Suddenly there was the sound of someone running and panting. Miss Kelsey saw Jimmy's lanky body slip into a back seat. She didn't know whether to notice him or not. She had tried so hard to make this Bible school helpful to the mountain boys and girls. She loved the mountain children, and more than anything else she wanted to help them love the Bible. She had had great hopes for Jimmy, but now on the fourth day he had disappointed her and hadn't arrived until twelve o'clock. There he was! His clothes were messy, his face streaked with dirt, though they had talked so much about being clean. There were scratches on his face, too. He looked as though he had been fighting. Miss Kelsey was discouraged indeed.

Jimmy wanted to say something. "I got here, Miss Kelsey. Will it count? Will it be a perfect attendance?"

"Where you been?" asked the other children. That was a fair question. Whether it "counted" or not depended upon where he had been.

Jimmy stood up and told his story. Every child turned around to look. The story grew more exciting every minute. Then at last, at last, the climax—"The doctor says he'll put new skin on the baby's burns. It'll be all right. But it ought to be in a cradle, not crawling on the floor."

Long after the time had come for the mountain children to go home, they sat in the pine shack, making plans. Jimmy had been the first to say he guessed he wouldn't make a bench. He guessed he'd use his good lumber for a cradle. Miss Kelsey seemed pleased with the idea.

"Mose could teach us to make a cradle if he was a-mind to," said Jonathan.

Miss Kelsey was appointed to find out "if he was a-mind to." One by one the girls decided that the dresses they were making for themselves could wait. The Carey baby needed smooth sheets in the cradle and some new clothes.

Jimmy had never been so happy in his life as when he and the other boys set to work making the cradle for the Carey baby.

As for Granny, when she heard what Jimmy had done, she said, "He's learning the Bible and learning it good."

—*Gertrude Jenness Rinden. From "Around the World with the Bible."*

$\mathcal{A}$ First Thanksgiving

IT WAS Sunday morning in early September. The church bells in Glenview had not yet begun to ring, but Paul was eager to be on his way. He said to Mother and Father, "I promised Miss Leslie I would be there early. Our class is going to paint, and I want to help get things ready. Mr. Harry doesn't like it when we carry water through the hall after classes start."

Paul lost no time going the three blocks to the church. Ahead of him a man was entering the side door. Paul was certain it was Mr. Harry.

"Guess I'll go in the front door," he decided. "He's sure to tell me I'm too early. As if I didn't know when I'm supposed to come!"

Inside the building Paul started down the hall only to see the man walking ahead of him. "Good morning!" he called, but there was no reply.

Paul walked briskly past the man and spoke again. Still there was no answer, so Paul turned. He stopped in surprise. The man was not Mr. Harry at all! He was a stranger.

Paul grinned at his own mistake and when the man smiled, he smiled in return and said, "Good morning!"

In the second grade classroom Miss Leslie was arranging the reading table.

"Here I am," Paul announced. "What shall I do first?"

Soon he was busy putting fresh paper on the easel and preparing paints and brushes and water.

"I know what I'll paint," he told Miss Leslie. "Something my hands did this summer. I did it with all my might, too, like the Bible verse says."

He dipped his brush into the green paint and sketched peas and beans. He dipped it into the red and made tomatoes and radishes like those he had planted and tended in his garden.

When Lucy arrived, Paul said, "Why don't you paint something your hands did?"

Lucy said, "I want to paint about my uncle. This summer when I visited him in the country, he used his hands to do about a hundred things for me. Best of all, I liked the swing he made."

Lucy painted herself swinging high up among the thick branches of the big oak tree.

Everyone in the class had a turn to paint, and when all the pictures were hung along the wall, Miss Leslie said, "Now we will have the story."

Paul and the others rushed to sit beside her. At that moment George tripped over a chair and crashed headlong into the easel.

The easel tilted toward the floor and toppled over with a bang, breaking the two front legs.

Red paint splashed in one direction, green paint in another. Yellow, brown, and blue paint made puddles on the floor. Water and broken glass seemed everywhere. Miss Leslie and some of the boys brought cloths.

"Mr. Harry won't like this extra work," Paul worried.

"Accidents will happen," Miss Leslie said cheerfully. "Mr. Harry won't even know about this one because. . ."

Before she could finish, a man carrying a mop and pail

came into the room. Paul stared in astonishment. It was the stranger!

Miss Leslie spoke to the man as if she knew him. "Oh, thank you for coming. You must have been waiting for us to need you."

The newcomer seemed to know Miss Leslie and not to mind that the paints and water were spilled. Without a word he mopped the floor. When he left, he took the easel with him. The children said, "Thank you," but his only answer was another smile.

The children gathered around Miss Leslie.

"Who is he? How did he know we needed him?"

"Doesn't he ever talk?"

"Where is Mr. Harry? Why didn't he come?"

Miss Leslie tried to answer all their questions at once. "Mr. Harry has moved. His son is sick and needs him. The stranger is Mr. Gregorfsky, the new caretaker. He has been in America only a short time and knows only a few words of our language. I think he doesn't try to speak because he is afraid someone may laugh at his mistakes. He knows everyone can understand a smile. He wants to be your friend."

The following Sunday Paul discovered the mended easel. Mr. Gregg, as the children called him, had nailed a board across the back of it to make a double one. "Look," Paul said, "now two of us can paint at the same time!"

Lucy went to the window. "And he fixed the shade so it pulls up and down without sticking."

The children were sure Mr. Gregg was their friend.

When Lucy suggested, "Let's make a surprise for him," George remembered the paintings. "We could show our pictures to him."

Paul spoke up exictedly. "I know! Let's help Mr. Gregg learn some of our words. We can point to something in a picture and tell him the word, and he can say it."

The others liked the idea. The next Sunday there were fifteen teachers and one pupil in the class.

Lucy taught the first word. She pointed to the picture of the rope swing her uncle had made for her. "Swing," she said.

"Swing," repeated Mr. Gregg. He said it so well the children chorused, "That's good!"

Quickly he learned the words "book," "garden," and "flower." Paul pointed to the peas, beans, tomatoes, and radishes in his picture. "These are vegetables," he told Mr. Gregg.

Mr. Gregg repeated slowly after him, "Wedge-tables." Then, because it did not sound right, he said it again, "Wedge-tables."

No one laughed. Then Mr. Gregg laughed. "My tongue, it go wrong." But he tried the word again and again until it was right.

Paul and the children were as proud of Mr. Gregg's learning as he was. They put pictures of some of the hard words into a scrapbook for him, a "Book About Helpers." They cut the pictures from magazines and pasted one on each page. Soon Mr. Gregg could pronounce each word in the book—postman, milkman, grocer, doctor, carpenter, engineer.

Meanwhile, Mr. Gregg found things to do for the children. He painted their reading table, put up coat hooks, made extra cupboard shelves.

One afternoon in late October Paul saw Mr. Gregg raking leaves. "Could I help?" he called.

Mr. Gregg pointed to an extra rake. "Sure."

While they worked, Paul suddenly asked, "Do you have any children like me?"

Mr. Gregg held up two fingers. "Have Stephen, ten. Have Anna, five. And have wife."

"Where are they?"

"City. Friend's house."

"Why don't they live with you?"

"No house."

Paul did not understand. What did Mr. Gregg mean, "no house"? Didn't everyone have a house?

On the next Sunday he asked Miss Leslie, "Why doesn't Mr. Gregg have a house?"

"Perhaps there are no more empty houses in Glenview," said Miss Leslie.

Later that morning when the class talked about Thanksgiving celebrations of long ago and now, Paul seemed puzzled.

"Mr. Gregg ought to be thankful on his first Thanksgiving in America, but how can he be thankful with no house and his family far away in the city?"

"Perhaps the class may help find the answer to your question," Miss Leslie said.

The class knew what they wanted to do. They wanted to bring Mr. Gregg's family to him at Thanksgiving. They wanted to find a house for them in Glenview. But how could boys and girls ever get money for railway tickets and find a house and furniture?

"Thanksgiving is almost here now," moaned Paul, as he counted the remaining days. "What can we do?"

"I can ask my parents to help," said Lucy.

"So can I," said all the others.

When the parents and older brothers and sisters heard what the second grade planned for Mr. Gregg, it seemed that everyone in the church wanted to give him a happy first Thanksgiving.

One of the fathers said, "My office building has an apartment at the top with four nice rooms and a kitchen. New wallpaper and linoleum will help make it a comfortable home."

The high school class offered to wash the windows and woodwork in the new home. The young people wanted to buy the dishes. The women's class collected money for tickets. Some families brought chairs, a dresser, and table.

When one family asked to buy the Thanksgiving dinner,

Paul thought of something the second grade could do. "Let's buy a new tablecloth for the Thanksgiving dinner," he suggested.

The next day after school a committee from the class went with Miss Leslie to the store. With their offering money they bought some pretty material. Miss Leslie cut it into the correct sizes for a cloth and napkins, and the children pulled threads and made wide fringed borders on each piece.

When Mr. Gregg next stopped in their room, he eagerly shared his news. "Stephen and Anna and Mother come tomorrow!"

When he left, Paul remarked with satisfaction, "Mr. Gregg looks thankfuller and thankfuller."

After the holiday, Mr. Gregg came again. He said to the children, "Every day it is Thanksgiving for my family now."

Paul and the other children and Miss Leslie were pleased. They knew they had helped to make that Thanksgiving.

—Elizabeth Allstrom. From "The Round Window."

A NEW WORD IN THE STORY

Gregorfsky   greh-GORF-skee